LAND OF
DAHORI

LAND O[F]

Tales of New Guine[a]

J. B. LIPPINCOTT COMPAN[Y]

DAHORI

by Olaf Ruhen

PHILADELPHIA & NEW YORK

CONTENTS

INTRODUCTION

THE Land of Dahori *—it is a derisive term: the Land of By and By; the Land of Mañana; the stronghold of postponement. "Dahori," they say: "Not yet; presently; in a little while." It is a land stretching after a long sleep; a land whose mind says, "Sleep again"; whose heart says, "Rest awhile"; whose hands are heavy in inaction. When you leave it behind you the brown eyes smile at you and the people say, "Ba mahuta, Taubada. Ba mahuta." It is the world's loveliest farewell: "May you sleep, Big Man. May you sleep."

But for me "dahori" has another meaning which underlies and gives force and vigor to the idea of postponement; and for me New Guinea is truly the Land of Tomorrow. For the people who coined the word "dahori" were the Motu people, a race of seamen-navigators; and words are travelers too. And among that other great race of seamen-navigators, the Polynesians, the word "tahira," which is almost the same word, means not only the "day before yesterday," but also the "day after tomorrow."

So, my "Land of Dahori," for me, if not for the purists, is the Land of By and By, the Land of the Day Before Yesterday and the Land of the Day After Tomorrow all in one.

I came first to New Guinea casually, by accident, covering for

* Alternative spellings are: Dohore, Dohori.

vii

a group of Australian periodicals the story of a millionaire-philan-thropist's introduction of sheep to the potentially rich pastures of the Central Highlands. My time was limited; but such was the impact of the country that before I had been there two days I was making arrangements for my return. And I returned again and again. On my second trip I traveled some fourteen thousand miles within the boundaries of the country; I accompanied patrols which made the first contacts with three different tribes of Stone Age men; I traveled with natives in their own manner and I left with reluctance.

My reasons for returning were manifold. In the first place I was amazed to find a country so diverse; a country where on the higher slopes the European oak is familiarly at home with the buttercup, the forget-me-not, the daisy and the wild strawberry; where the European lark and the blackbird hold a curious association with the hornbill and the birds of paradise; where strawberries and bananas are cultivated in the same plot and produce fruit in every season of the year.

From the air my first sight of New Guinea's central valleys approximated my memories of western France—similar tree-lined roads, clustered houses and gardens, concentrated cultivation, all of it primitive, but in general pattern amazingly like the world we know. I was to find later that specimens of the flora were identical with, variously, some from the Himalayas, from New Zealand, from Australia and the sub-antarctic as well as from Europe. I was overpowered with color and the songs of birds and the majesty of the mountains. And I was amazed at the level of aesthetic attainment achieved by natural man.

Primarily I had been interested in the experiment of sheep breeding. The philanthropist, now Sir Edward Hallstrom, was first interested in New Guinea's birds, for he is an avid and most successful collector. His sheep experiment was provoked by his experience of finding, in the near-freezing temperatures of the mountain mornings, a large percentage of naked children wheezing and coughing and suffering from chest complaints. His idea was to introduce sheep and teach the natives how to care for them, how to use the wool, weave it and make it into blankets and warm clothing.

Examined from civilization's standpoints, from within the boundaries of a civilized city, it seemed an excellent idea. On the spot I immediately conceived doubts about the whole scheme. In the first place, the natives already had furs and textiles of their own, and I felt there must be reason why they did not use them for clothing. There was.

In those mountains, the villages were perched upon the spurs, primarily for defense reasons; but also because, if the people were to build in the valleys, they would have become subject to many more of the fevers and diseases which their beautiful land unfortunately harbors in some quantity. Nearly every village was a long way from water, and a supply for drinking had to be carried each day in bamboo vessels.

Now if these people were to be provided with blankets, it would have become essential for them to wash them, the more frequently because of their own protective coverings of smoked lard or pandanus oil. Thus it would have become necessary to shift the houses to the valleys, to stop using the oil, to wear clothes. They would have to assume with the blankets, in short, an entirely new way of life.

I did not condemn Sir Edward's approach to the problem. It was at least a sincere and a dynamic approach, and while I did not feel it would achieve the success hoped for it, I felt it would underline some of the problems, and perhaps stimulate some other activity. Its effect on myself personally was to start me on a line of inquiry which I have never been able or willing to drop.

The subsequent, total effect of New Guinea was to upset all my preconceived ideas of human development, and consequently to promote a rather restless search for truths to replace the conceptions I discarded. This book contains the results of that search, and the episodes and incidents which make up the sum of its contents are all based upon truth, so far as I have been able to establish it. They all represent a fairly accurate reporting of human experience, and where the experience was not my own, or not within the command of my own senses, I had it from the principal actor in his own words and I confirmed it independently.

The limitations of experience being what they are, a majority of the incidents would come into the second category.

LAND OF
DAHORI

The Legend

*T*HERE *are no destination signs on the road. It stretches endlessly to the horizon. If at a moment of time you find yourself on such a highway, how can you know where you are going? There are those who, carefreely, travel the road for the enjoyment of the journey; for the sting and tingle of the wind in the face; for the speed and the passing. But for the rest of us each byroad, each fork poses a problem.*

Where am I? Where are you? Where are we all?—and Where is civilization? We cannot tell, with surety. Our common destination is simply a subject for theorizing and argument. But there is this: If we know where we have been, and if we choose our direction, then we can hazard a rough guess at the objective.

Then where have we been?

We have come to this spot we call the Twentieth Century from the Stone Age, and it seems to me that if we knew something of that age of our ancestors, something of the people who lived in it, something of the way they thought and conducted their lives, something of their laws and their morals and their philosophy, something of their standards, their abhorrences, their development and their ambitions, then we should know something of ourselves. For me this is the greater lesson of history; and for me history is not a period circumscribed by a small score of centuries.

In the remoter corners of the Pacific the Stone Age is still in existence.

Notably, it contains an island called New Guinea, an island greater in size than any other in the world except for the bare and barren stretches of Greenland. New Guinea has an area of 330,000 square miles, an area more than six times that of England, yet it supports a bare two million people. It is situated between the tropical north of Australia and the Equator, only a little way from the over-populated East, and very much under the acquisitive eye of Indonesia as, for a time, it was under the acquisitive eye of Japan.

It is inhabited by a people peculiar to itself, a people markedly different from the indigenes of either Australia or Indonesia, a people markedly unlike any others anywhere, yet not at all homogenous. Ethnologists distinguish three ethnical elements with some clarity, classifying them as: Papuans proper, diffused over the whole region; Negritos, who have been found over most districts in the interior; and Melanesians. There are also traces of an occasional Polynesian influx, and, much more abundantly, of Malayans. There are also other source elements present in small quantities which have largely escaped ethnological notice.

About 1870 Count Luigi Maria d'Albertis, a balding, fork-bearded Italian naturalist who went barefooted, and dressed, native-style, in a minimum of clothing, classified an enormous proportion of the flora and fauna of the country. He reported that in a harbor on the north coast he saw four or five Arab dhows and several Malayan praus trading for slaves, for skins of the bird of paradise, trepang, ebony, mother-of-pearl and turtle shell.

The reference to slaves was interesting. The trade had undoubtedly been carried on for thousands of years, and it was responsible for taking population elements in both directions. Sick or ailing slaves that had crewed the dhows would be left behind; Arab masters uncaringly contributed their own progeny to the future com-

munity, and by one means or another members of half the races of the known world must, over the centuries, have added their leaven of blood components to the New Guinea population.

There is consequently a great diversity of types. But in spite of the variety of contributing elements the greatest internal demarcation between the indigenous peoples today is that which separates the static tribes of the interior from the mobile, adventurous, trade-hungry tribes of the coast.

Generally speaking it is still true that the people of New Guinea and its outlying neighbors are born and live and make their tiny marks and die much in the fashion of our own ancestors two or three thousand years behind us. Their motives seem to be the motives of our ancestors; perhaps they are the same as ours. The influences that mold their lives molded the lives of our forebears many many years ago, and set us on the road we travel.

New Guinea itself is a not inconsiderable land. By the standards of today or those of our immediate yesterday it is wealthy; and its people are potentially rich. Each little brown man—small in stature because of unwise infant feeding—holds, on the average, 120 times as many broad acres as an Englishman.

Less than a century ago, our people generally measured land in terms of its ability to produce a vegetable growth; and we ourselves are still in this habit. Yet our need today is not mainly for grass, or for the fruits of the field. Our greatest need is for electrical power. In terms of power potential there is no more wealthy land in the world than New Guinea. Its mountains reach fourteen thousand feet into the skies between narrow seacoasts; and on these mountains one of the greatest average rainfalls in the world teems down.

Nor is this all. The rainy season on the one side of the land occupies the alternate half of the year to that of the rainy season on the other, so that a properly integrated hydroelectric system could work at full capacity the whole year round.

No other area in the world evinces so many signs of geo-thermal activity. There are hundreds and hundreds of volcanoes, boiling pools and mud springs, and hot and cold geysers, each one of them a potential for easily tapped power. The sun's heat is received here as almost nowhere else on earth. And the oil below the surface has been held against production needs these many years.

New Guinea, then, is a jewel of the future. But it remains as yet a museum of the past. And before the inevitable transformation there are lessons to learn from the country and its people.

We have, at best, a poor enough idea of our ancestors. We have a few stone tools, a few cave paintings. Were these, in their paucity, representative of the total ingenuity of our forebears? Those scientists who work from the particular to the general, who find a thighbone and reconstruct a mammoth are, in the face of other evidence, prone to come to the conclusion that they were.

Once, on a minor expedition to New Guinea, I sailed seven hundred miles up that great river of the north coast, the Sepik, into territory that had been only lightly traversed; and there I met three tribes of men who had never met any white men. Nor had their ancestors within the very wide limits of communal memory. These people had not even heard of white men. And they were so remote from civilization that, given salt, they tasted it and threw it in the river, contrary to the forecasts of men who had in their time met other unknown tribes. They were also remote from, and unknown to, their neighbors of the seacoast. They were people of whose lives the insularity was complete.

And they were Stone Age men. Their tools were stone adzes. They had the bow and the arrow, the bone dagger, the stone ax. They worked beautifully in wood, building carved canoes of which the lifetime, in that climate, would be little more than a year. They had no metals, nor did they have the wheel.

But they were potters and weavers, and their fabrics, woven of straw, were fine enough to keep mosquitoes at bay and stout enough to contain the family pigs and poultry. Among their artifacts were spinning-tops, on which they gambled, apparently; and tweezers for the decoration of fabric and the elimination of whiskers, built most delicately and wonderfully of bird bone. These artifacts would not have lived through the years to meet the eyes of a future generation of archaeologists; but the adzes and axes would have stood the test of time. From such enduring relics the picture of the people would have been an incomplete one.

I think therefore the picture we have built of our own ancestors is also incomplete. It does not even begin to give us the story of their ingenuity. More, and much more, it does not begin to give us the philosophy that gave birth, through generations, to our own.

My friends in New Guinea were lately head-hunters. No building was properly begun, no canoe efficiently launched, unless the head of a friend or an enemy lay under the piling, or dripped its blood over the prow. To us, this is a reprehensible custom. Yet among these people were men who understood the power of the philosophy behind these sacrifices. They knew of reasons impossible to deny, of logic incontrovertible.

First among these reasons was the responsibility of government, and the race-preserving necessity for it to establish and maintain power. To understand it requires a brief understanding of the island's way of life.

The more venturesome tourist, passing the remoter New Guinea village, is apt to comment adversely and unjustifiably on the lazy habits of the villagers. A majority of the men, perhaps, are lazing about the huts in the sunshine, chipping abstractedly at canoe decoration, or fiddling with insignificant lengths of cordage. But if the tourist were to pass again at midnight, if the moon happened to be full, he might, by observing, for instance, the activity of the fishing fleet, be constrained to revise his ideas. For the day is one of twenty-four hours in New Guinea, and there is a task and a duty for every hour of the day.

It takes a good man to make his living from the bush, to feed himself and his family, to clothe them all and give them shelter. It takes a worker who uses at least as much of his year as, say, the factory worker. The villager has not the labor-saving devices of civilization. If he shoots a possum, he must make himself another arrow, for he cannot go to the store and buy one as you would a cartridge. A fishhook is a work of infinite patience and skill, but it is easily lost and easily broken. The making of a meal of sago occupies many man-hours of unremitting work.

But the primitive man is equal to the task. Had he not been, he would have died. This competence brings its own dangers. For it makes him independent, and the independent man cannot be governed. Yet the elders of the tribe, without the protection of government, would themselves die; for their own skills in the debilitation of their age are no longer equal to the task of wrestling with Nature. And the independent man must be induced to shoulder his responsibilities. Therefore it is in the nature of the elders to enforce government, even as with us. The village elders have to forge a weapon they can use to enforce the tribal laws. They have chosen the weapon of fear.

Even today we cannot govern without fear. For all our advances we must still use this primitive weapon. But it is subtly changed. For the fear used by the civilized is an economic fear—a healthy fear that makes the breadwinner flex his muscles, and develops the adolescent, and protects the weak, and encourages the child. In such a community as you will find in New Guinea, where each man wrests his separate living from the sea or the river or the forests or the fields, there is no economic fear.

Nor is economic fear comprehensible to them. For a weapon to command respect, its potentialities must be clearly or at least adequately understood.

Therefore the New Guinea elders govern with the aid of a physical fear. It is the only weapon they possess. It is called witchcraft, and magic, and sangguma; and it is called bloody-mindedness pure and simple.

Stand in this yam patch at this unpropitious time, and the gods will demand your life; and the elders are the instruments of the gods.

Let this woman look on this ceremony sacred to men, and as the gods have decreed it she will nevermore look on anything else, at any time, in any place. The gods have spoken, and the elders enforce their will.

This was the beginning of legislation: These bananas are handy and accessible, and the elders may enjoy them; but only if the younger people are excluded. The banana patch becomes taboo to those who have not passed the full initiation tests of the elders. One youngster breaks the taboo and dies. The bananas were not worth the life. But the preservation of all the laws intact demanded it.

These people are not apes who have lost their tails. They are of the jungle—and so are we. And if you live with them you will be reminded, again and again, of their counterparts who live in other settings. You will grow to know them.

Kirong, the old man with the ravaged, crocodile-bitten leg, is an incorrigible humorist. Nataru is boring, and tells long tales of his youth. Yabu is wise, but shy of expressing an opinion. Sibobu is a braggart. Akimi can work with his hands, but has no opinions. Ura steals other men's wives, but all forgive him for it. Daisa is religious. He spends many hours communing with his ancestors and his gods, asking for guidance. Mahanga pretends religion, so that he may advise his contemporaries. Animari is a storyteller, and Watsiup sings songs on nights of feasting when the moon is full.

A long time ago, when I was a small boy stealing a daily hour from school to spend it in the near-by green New Zealand bush, I listened again and again to the poetry of a Maori forester, who told me some of the stories he had had from his ancestors. It seemed to me then, as it seems to me now, that there was truth here. But the Maoris are a century removed from the reality of their tribal being. Their laws and covenants, once enforced and administered with ferocity, now make pretty stories. Their art is rationalized to decorate steepled churches and flat-roofed cottages. The truth is still there, but it is hard to see through the deepening lacquer of our own applied traditions.

But in New Guinea the patrols go out several times a year and find a new people. They are people living entirely to themselves, administering their own laws, speaking a language no others can understand. There are, perhaps, five hundred languages in New Guinea. Iatmol, which covers the largest area, a huge tract of land near the mouth of the Sepik River, is understood by few more than fifty thousand people. Makolkol, perhaps the smallest, may not be understood by more than fifty. The Makolkol, who are believed to live in trees, have made brief contacts with the white; but none has been maintained. As the story goes a white man once shot a mother of the Makolkol people, and brought her in, wounded, with her child—a rather excessive attempt to obtain a rare specimen. But they both died.

There is little reason to doubt that the Makolkol have stories, legends, laws, a reason for living, and a goal in the afterlife.

Here, once, were we: living in trees, each man of us the enemy of every man outside the tribe.

What kind of people were we? Perhaps the Makolkol can tell us. Perhaps we are still not so very different from the Makolkol. Perhaps we have come only a little way along this road that has seemed so long. If we can mentally retrace that way we have come, then, perhaps, knowing the direction of our journey, we can establish our goal, visualize it, work toward it.

To this end, these stories are my effort. For in the story the essential man lives, as he cannot in an anthropological record. The record is for the scientist. These stories are designed for others.

Before government came magic. Before the premier or the president came the chief; but before the chief, and ruling him still, was the witch doctor, the fakir, the holy man, the power behind the throne.

In the excessive use of power the witch doctor succumbed to temptation and became malevolent. But in the time of the establishment of power he was a different man, far-seeing and wise, if not benign.

The establishment of power enabled the family to develop, and the family was the progenitor of the tribe; and the tribes amalgamated to become nations, and the nations developed our civilization.

The Husbandmen

WHO was Rulago? Where did he live, and when? Who were his father and his mother, and who his brothers and sisters? How did he come by the things that he knew? And who were his friends, and who his teachers? Was he in love, perhaps, when he was young? And was he lonely when he was old? Is there not someone who remembers?

There is, to be sure, a song they sing in the gardens at the time of planting. It is just a little song, with a little lilt in the singing that lightens the burden of the work and stays its tediums. And the song is nothing, for it has no meaning, but the work is lighter when the people sing it. And so sometimes the men, as they set the seed in the soil hoed high from the garden paths, sing to themselves:

> *"Rulago and me, Rulago and me,*
> *Rulago knows of the seed of the tree;*
> *Rulago knows, Rulago knows,*
> *The seed and the tree are Rulago's."*

But this is little to hold and keep as the memory of a man. There is a little more, for the insistence of our hopes can strengthen the whispers from the past into the knowledge of a strong man who could fight with the cunning of twenty. So we know that he lived by himself in the forest—if indeed he lived and was of the earth at all; for there are some who think that Rulago was a demigod and a nothingness, and dead with the gods themselves. Yet people did things because he willed it.

And if, like Rulago, a man goes apart from the people and sits by himself, and sees the clear visions of truth unclouded by the commerce of social thought and the striving for a diversity of ends, he may yet uncover wonders as great as those which were Rulago's. If his mind is concerned with these things he may even find Rulago, for there is a trace here, a sign there, a memory further off; and all the many years of time may be bridged by such a man if he has patience and the hope of coming to an end. There are memories of Rulago in the forest, and a stone which was Rulago's in the river.

The river is the Sasato River which runs between today's villages of Bagusini and Dumdain. The Sasato empties into the Buasi, and the Buasi runs between Busama and Buang. But in the days of Rulago there was no village at Bagusini or at Dumdain; nothing at all at Busama or Buang. The villages came later, after the gardens appeared and the clearings in the forest; and the forest was virgin when Rulago was a child.

The people were hunters only, moving swiftly from place to place and seeking the wild fruits, the plantains and the taro and the figs in their season. When there was a plenty they ate more than their fill, but often and often there was little or nothing. There were no paths through the forest, certainly not wide paths and good, and at nights the people secured themselves however they could against their enemies. And the enemies, too, ranged as far as they could for their food, and slept uneasily.

The people lived together, and moved together with the seasons from one place of last year's good eating to the next; and before he came to his manhood Rulago was one of them. He was the first of all the boys of his age to learn the secrets of weapons and the rituals of good hunting. He learned the trees and the grasses and the flowers; which killed, which cured, and which were good to eat. He was the most silent at his initiation; his flesh did not flinch from the knife, and therefore they carved the patterns of his acceptance deep and heavy in his skin.

He was wise and old in the head, and soon he was bigger than all the men; yet he looked young. When he slept or when he sat his limbs lay heavy; and when he was hunting he was tireless. The mountains strengthened his shoulders and his thighs; the rivers deepened his chest. He was the first of his years to be admitted to the lower councils; and he was the first, too, to lose his friends among the elders.

He was a strong youth and quick on his feet, and handy in a fight; and he learned quickly all that the old men could teach him. Too quickly, too, he learned the things that they would not teach him. He saw, as he was meant to see, the thing that had been Agilop, who was taken in adultery with Aos, the wife of Ruami, the headman, shuffling piteously three days with the people as they moved through the forest; the fingers of his hands broken and swollen, his tongue pinned in his throat with palm needles, and swollen till his mouth could not contain it, his eardrums stabbed with thorns and his body racked with pain.

And he saw the people, no better themselves and no worse, add to Agilop's pain and suffering, and laughingly bid the children watch, and encourage them to add their own small torments until Agilop died of his anguish. And when Aos dropped out from the march and was not seen again he knew that the elders had also had their way.

And so he learned that a community needs law, and that the implementation of law is dependent upon fear. He learned that if there is no fear the lawmakers are threatened, and are themselves afraid, and when the suspicion of this knowledge in him came to the elders he learned to be careful of his tongue and his ways, for rulers in fear are rulers about to strike, quickly and blindly and savagely and often.

So Rulago, who thus began to know his people and hence to love them, who knew no fear and needed no laws, parted from them all and stayed alone in the forest.

The people went on and soon forgot him. But Rulago had the silence of the days and the forest, and he learned from his eyes and his ears and his nose and his tongue and the tips of his fingers. He stayed alone in the valleys where the Sasato joins the Buasi, and the trees were his friends.

He ate well, for there were many fish in the river, and he was quick with a spear, and he made twine from the bark of tree roots and braided it into net. He knew where the birds nested, and how to hunt the snakes and the lizards and all the little animals. He waited till the fruits and the berries came to their best development and ate them at his leisure.

At the place where the Sasato pours its flood into the Buasi a mighty rock marks the junction, and the rivers break against its sides. Where the whirlpools boil away from it into the main current, twisting and turning like a school of cornered eels among the reefs, and boiling up white and fierce and silent, the rock stands sheer to the sky, higher than the highest trees. To landward its contours are more kindly, and the approaches are easy from any direction. An enemy could take a man here at his leisure. But there are ledges and clefts on this landward side that make a shelter, and here Rulago spent many of his days with his thoughts and his dreams.

It was here that he tipped his arrows, and laid up his twine and braided his nets, and here, if he had no such work to do, he sat and watched the ants running always on their errands, or the lizards, blue and gold and black. There was a peace on the rock that was the peace of a guarded home for him, and its familiar substance lightened his solitude.

When people came to his domain he kept them under observation, yet he saw to it that he himself was hidden. He covered up the traces of his hunting and walked where he would not rouse the chattering parrots to a rage. And thus he preserved his solitude many years in these valleys, until he made himself kin with the earth and the trees, and in the strength of his kinship he made a garden.

That is to say he cleared away a little bush here and there, and he planted a root or a seed, and considered it while it grew. And when the fruit was ripe or the root ready for lifting he found that in certain places there grew yams of great size, and that in others the bean pods were long and full, and the plantains softer to the mouth, and taller of habit, keeping more of their fruits from the reach of the little ground animals. He found that good fruits grew better in bigger gardens, from which the shadowing trees were cleared away to lay them open to the sun.

Now there was too much in the gardens for the use of Rulago alone, and his heart was drawn to the people he had left. For he knew that when they learned to make gardens for themselves they could stay in one place and grow fat among the fruits, and nevermore be driven to travel daily into new fears. But he knew that if he went back to live among them now they would fear him, and the elders would remove him from the tribe and from life. They would not allow the people to listen to his talk of gardens.

The people in their travels came upon the gardens of Rulago and they said, "Who is this that has cut away the trees? And who is this that has set stakes for the beans to climb upon? And who has set the pit-pit and the sugar growing in lines?"

The women huddled in groups and held the children close, and the men also showed their fear, but the hand of famine had gripped the tribe; their bellies were lean and their need desperate; so they stripped the plants quickly and ran away through the forest looking behind them.

And Rulago, watching, had been sore at heart, though he knew well enough that this must be the way of it. Yet he was glad that his labors had saved them from the extremities of this time of hunger. In that year the people did not return to the garden, and the good food continued to grow and be good, only to fall at last to the possums and the flying foxes.

So he thought of a plan to bring the people themselves to the making of gardens; and for this he made a charm that was strong magic. From the fibres of pandanus roots he made twine, and from the twine he made two carrying bags. In the bag that he carried in his right hand he put seeds and the bulbs of lilies and the shoots of sugar. But in the bag that he carried in his left hand he put all manner of charms, each of them strong smelling and pungent, a smell to stay in the nostrils and leap to the memory. He made some from the skin of the cuscus and some of the beaks of hornbills, and one was a tobacco pipe made from bamboo and a dried bean. The smells joined together, and carried on the wind and traveled quickly.

Now when the people traveled to leeward of his gardens Rulago made a sing-sing, and his voice carried through the trees; and when he raised his right hand above his head, with the carrying bag of seeds and shoots and roots he sang of planting, and of things growing, and of the sun and the moon and the rain. And when he raised his left hand with the carrying bag of charms his songs became incantation, and the smell of the charms followed the sounds of his singing through the forest down the lazy wind, and stopped the people where they traveled.

"Who is this that sings in the forest?" people said. And they said, "What are these smells that come on the wind?" And most of the people had great fear, and the warriors would seize their weapons and run swiftly upwind to find the singer who spread the sound and the smell of magic through the trees.

Always they would find a garden in their path, and the beans in it long and bursting, or the yams big and mighty, so that the sight halted them while they marveled; and Rulago would escape quickly by ways that he knew. Always they found a garden, and no singer. And the warriors would call the people and set a watch while the women stripped the plants; and as quickly as they could they left that place with their booty.

Rulago sorrowed, because he had set them a lesson and they would not heed. But he tried and he tried, and when in the second year the bananas ripened in a garden that had been robbed of its yams, he called the people back once more with his chanting and the smells of his magic. For many years he set his gardens and called the people; but they would not learn, and he knew still that if he were to go among them he would quickly die, because they would fear him.

But his magic was sovereign, and he was strong in his faith of its power and practiced it with constancy even when the people were far beyond the boundaries of his valleys. And always when he had made a garden he took his carrying bags, the seeds in his right hand and the charms in his left, and went to his rock above the rapids where the Sasato leaps to its union with the Buasi; and here he made his sing-sing and exhorted his charms, and the smell of his magic lingered, and stayed strong about that place.

A season came when Rulago set out a garden, and when it was young, before it was half planted, the people came by accident upon it, taking him by surprise, so that his speed and his skill alone stood between him and an instant discovery. And the people found the seeds of his garden waiting to be planted, lying on the ground and the smell of his charms over them, mingled with the smell of the new-burned brush and the strong fragrance of the new-turned earth, and they read his urgent flight in the evidence of his footprints in the new-tilled soil.

They picked up the seeds, and they were the seeds of the plants

that gave them food, as they knew well; but the people did not know
about planting them in the cover of the soil. But where the new
plants were showing above-ground they pulled some up, and found
the seed, and the seeds were all at the one stage of growth. Among
each other the people talked, and they said, "We, too, could do this
thing, if we knew the sing-sing, and if we had the charms that have
left their smell upon this place."

For the first time it seemed good to the people to till the ground,
and tend the plants, and keep a garden for themselves. At this time
they gave a name and an identity to the gardener in the forest, calling him Rulago, for the name of his childhood had passed beyond
memory with the youth himself. They called him Rulago, and they
pictured him an admirable man, very wise and very strong, with
ways beyond their comprehension. Yet they feared him, too, as men
do the unknown.

And Rulago, lying hid, guessed at their thoughts and was glad,
but still he knew that if he were to come among them they would
fear him, and kill him, and run away; because they would not understand such a gift from a man of power. So he held apart, and for
many years thereafter he grew his gardens and made his sing-sing
and kept his charms renewed and their smell strong and pungent.
People came more often to the valleys, and they had less fear of the
gardens; but at nights they did not stay.

But the elders talked, and studied the gardens, and sometimes
they came upon the ground when it was newly cleared, and sometimes before the seed had sprouted, and they said, "We could make
a garden for ourselves, and grow yams and kau-kau if we had the
magic of Rulago, if we could sing the songs and use the charms."

Agola, the headman, said, "We must keep a lookout and stay near
this place, and when we smell the smell of the charms we must take
Rulago, and then his magic will be ours, and we will build a garden."

None of the elders took up the straws of argument to deny these words of logic. For the fear of Rulago had entered the bellies of them all, and threatened the people's honest fear of the lawgivers.

Now when the signs began to tell him how the people thought, and he knew that he was about to become a hunted one, Rulago went every day to the junction of the Sasato and the Buasi, and stood high against the sky on the clifftop facing the whirlpools that boiled away from the rivers' meeting; and he made his sing-sing every afternoon as the sun went to its setting. And when he raised his right hand with the carrying bag of seeds he shouted, and when he raised his left the smell of the charms spread through the forest, and people said, "That is the magic of Rulago."

And soon they knew very well that Rulago made his magic on the stone between the rivers.

One afternoon when all the warriors were together they heard the sing-sing and smelled the smell very close to hand; and they followed down the bank of the Sasato, and saw Rulago on top of the stone with his back to the land and his face to the water of the rivers, and the bag of charms raised high in his left hand, and the tools for working the garden at his feet.

They spread quietly across all the landward approaches to the rock, and crept forward to the edge of cover, and still Rulago did not move or turn his head. When all the men were ready, Farapo, the young man, the big man, the fastest of all the people, leaped up the rock, and they thought he had taken Rulago, but Rulago turned and held him.

When they saw this, all the men rushed forward to help Farapo, and to bind Rulago and take him as he was back to the people. But as they reached him Rulago twisted free and leaped like a bird from the rock, and plunged beneath the whirlpools at the base of the rock, and was gone.

In after years Farapo swore that an eagle had come and taken Rulago from his grasp, and of the others some said that Rulago himself was the eagle and changed before their eyes. For from that dizzy rock this was all they saw of Rulago, whom they feared: a movement in the air and the great bulk of a mighty man against the sky, then only the line of whirlpools at the rivers' joining.

But they stood there and smelled the strong smell of the charms, and at their feet they saw the two bags that Rulago had fashioned from the twine. First one warrior and then the other touched them, and then drew back, talking like a man in council while he waited for others to handle the bags.

Agola, the headman, took the bags by the butt, first one and then the other, and emptied them where everyone could see. And in one bag was all manner of seeds for planting, and bulbs of taro, and the jointed stems of vines. And in the other were the charms for planting, and the strong urgent smell of them was proof they were the true charms, and the warriors rejoiced because they knew at last they had taken the secret of the garden.

So they made their gardens and worked hard; and the fear of foodlessness was gone from them, and the elders had to bring new fears to strengthen the influence of the laws. Their gardens were bigger than the gardens Rulago had set for them, and the food they grew was better, and the yams were bigger and the plantains softer, and the sugar sweeter, and they were proud because they had taken this secret from the mighty Rulago.

And of Rulago there is only the stone in the Sasato River, and a little song they sing at planting time in the gardens; but this is a thing greater than it seems, and Rulago was long ago content.

The Woman
of Labu

THE light from the torch of coconut fronds in
Biria's left hand illumined the water that lay
within the range of her upraised spear, that
caressed her body up to her waist, that sheltered the fish she was
hunting. The light swelled and diminished, but within its protection
this only was her world, the water, and the sand beneath her feet,
the velvet air of night and her spear-armed self; and the things that
lay beyond the light lay also beyond her consciousness. Not quite all,
for the other woman was in her thoughts, the woman Ingat who at
this moment was likewise waist-deep in water, armed likewise with
a spear and a blazing torch. Biria had only to lift her eyes to see the
whereabouts of Ingat, the little woman; but she kept her concentration for the little world illumined by her torch, and the Ingat of her
thoughts was an intruder in that world.

Two fish swam lazily into the compass of the light, two good fish,
and one for the taking. The woman Biria, alert before, now poised
upon the brink of integrated action, the torch in her left hand continuing to rise to its zenith with the controlled lifting of her arm. In
her right hand the upraised spear was vibrant with readiness, yet
her tensed muscles were so controlled there was no alteration in the

rhythm of the water droplets sliding steady from its circlet of points.

For a moment she seemed to regard the fish with dispassion; and when she moved again her spear hand never quivered, but the blazing torch dropped swiftly and steadily almost to the water, its combustion strengthened by the movement, and its light confined.

When she stilled the torch the flame surged up, fat and rich once more, and in the sudden accession of light the fish were clearly to be seen, and her muscles loosened into a song of movement, and the spear thrust straight and true, and took the fatter, heavier fish upon its points. Torch in one hand, fish-bearing spear in the other, Biria turned and waded back through the little surf to walk to the big fire higher up the beach. When she turned, the little woman Ingat turned too, and came running with her torch and her empty spear.

"Oo-oo," she called. "He's a beauty. You have the eye for the fish. Three already! And I have none."

Thus and thus she always chattered, skipping sideways, careless of her torch and scattering sputtering brands along the beach, bright-eyed and noisy, and admiring the fish the like of which she saw every week of her life.

"Fish won't come on your spear by themselves," Biria snapped. "You can't catch fish on the beach here, out of the water."

Ingat was always the same, she thought. Ingat did little work, and what she did was not well done. The taking of fish was a game for her, all her tasks were games and all her days a happiness. Ingat scamped the work of a woman, and yet Ingat was well loved. Everyone had a smile for her; everyone stopped at her house for a word and a gossip, and shared good luck with her.

Some of the people were at the fire, the fishermen replenishing their torches, and others bringing wood, or stringing their fish, or just gossiping for the night's company. The firelit air carried a staccato of voices that ceased briefly while the people eyed the fish on Biria's spear; and then burst out again, mingling with the other sounds of the night, the frogs and the insects and the wood snapping in the heat. Beyond the influence of the firelight the beach stretched wide and white, darkening only under the shade of the trees, and by contrast, where the dancing pathway to the moon angled away from its edge, and went forever over the dark and dancing water.

Past the lines of the surf, for the full length of the beach, the bom-bom torches rose and fell, rose and fell, accenting the rhythm of the search; and with the movement each rubied light swelled and diminished, contracting to a spark-shedding minimum with movement, and expanding to a great orb of fresh-fed flame in the momentary halt above the water's surface.

And in this moment of light, if the fisherman was near by, you could see his body lit red and defiant against the glinting water, a brief vision of the hunter that in a second faded into a mass that was more of the mind than of the eye. Sometimes the fisher was a woman, and sometimes there was a glimpse of beauty as the light struck the upraised spear arm, the lifted breast beneath it, and the wet lap-lap swathed low on the belly.

Biria strung her fish with the others she had caught, and stooped to take a dry lap-lap from her billum, the head-net she wore wherever she went; but Ingat protested, loving the night and the movement of the night, and loath to go to the next experience.

"Once more," she cried. "Just once more. I haven't caught a fish."

Biria stopped, unwilling, her hand on the open billum, her firm program questioned; and Ingat began to plead.

"All right," said Biria; and already Ingat was running back to the gentle surf. Biria took a new torch, ready bound to hand, and lighted it at the fire and followed. Within minutes Ingat speared a little fish, and she laughed and called out, shouting and showing it to everyone, bragging like a little girl with her first skirt, although the fish was smaller than any of the three that had fallen to Biria. And Biria noted, sourly, that people paid attention too, and made jokes about little Ingat and her little fish. She was irritated, yet even while she felt this she wondered about herself, that Ingat, so friendly, and so rich in friends, should seek her company.

While they dressed, casually folding clean dry lap-laps over the wet ones, then slipping these away from underneath, she envied the figured cloth that Ingat kept for best, yet wore to the fishing. And her envy grew as Ingat, following a fashion new to the place, took a flower-patterned scarf and tied it about her neck so that her little breasts lay half-concealed within the bight of the cloth; for Biria had no such clothing.

When they were ready they wrapped the fish in taro leaves and placed them with their wet lap-laps in their corded billums, and swung the carrying straps to their foreheads, and went on their way. Biria was from the village of Labu, and Ingat from a smaller place in the hills beyond, so that their paths ran only a little way together before they separated. They talked awhile at this place of parting and Ingat said, "Not tomorrow, but the next day we will come to bom-bom the fish again. The moon is so big it is a shame to waste it."

They agreed on this, and Ingat said, "We'll meet here where the paths join, late in the afternoon, and walk together to the beach."

When she was away from Ingat, walking by herself on the bush path, Biria wondered why she had agreed. She felt no love for Ingat except when she was with her, but Ingat was her only friend, the only woman who sought her company. The rest, the women of her own village, only tolerated her. Sometimes she said hard things about Ingat, the useless woman, tiny and slight, and lazy as well. But when they were together Ingat made her happy, and sometimes they laughed together like children. There was no woman in Labu with whom she laughed.

The responsibility of meeting Ingat became a little burden in her mind, something useless to carry, and she wished she had not assented to the arrangement, but when the time came she was first at the junction of the paths, and she waited, but there was no sign of the little woman.

She sat for a long time; then because she was a woman who must ever have something to do, she went into a high place above the track and looked for frogs.

She found three good frogs and put them in her billum to take home to her family. Then she returned to the path but Ingat had not arrived.

"The woman must be dead," she thought. "Good enough for her."

She waited and waited, and it was nearly dark. As the wind died she heard the thin sound of a sing-sing, a faraway wailing that seemed to come from the village in the hills. She listened hard to try to make out the nature of the sing-sing, but the sound was too tenuous. It lay right at the very bounds of her hearing, so that the lift of the wind blotted it out, and the surge of the larger waves on the beach destroyed it.

"Ingat has died," she thought, "and this is the sing-sing for her death.

"I wonder," she thought, "just what was the manner of her dying."

And she thought of Ingat, the little woman, lying dead, her bubbling life still as a stone, and she became filled with sorrow.

"She was a good woman, though she worked little. She was my one good friend," she thought. And she began to rock herself backward and forward as she waited, squatting at the junction of the paths, but just at that time she heard something and looked up to see Ingat coming along the path; and immediately she was angry because Ingat was there, and was herself, and had not changed.

"They're making a sing-sing in your village," she said. "Why?"

"Oh, they make a sing-sing about nothing," Ingat answered lightly, and immediately she asked, "Have you waited long for me?"

Biria asked no more questions, but she thought this a strange thing that Ingat should not talk of the sing-sing. It could have been anything, it could have been nothing. But from what she had been able to hear, Biria thought the people had been singing a death.

However, they went together a little way along the path, and there was a place where they set a fire and cooked themselves some taro. Biria did most of the work while Ingat talked, and told all the gossip of the village. Once Biria lifted her head and said, "I hear a sing-sing. Surely there must be a sing-sing in your village"; but Ingat hardly glanced into the gathering dark, hardly stilled her busy tongue for a moment; and then she said, "I hear nothing."

And she went on with her tale of young Maiu, and how he was believed to have consummated an attachment he had for the wife of Animari, the headman, and how their place of assignation was beneath the floor of Animari's hut so that the lovers would be warned if the headman stopped snoring. There was much more of this and the talk went on and on, and though Biria felt she was doing most of the work, she loved it all.

It was very beautiful in that place, and there was a fragrance from the ginger lily and the strong heady smell of tropic earth, and something salty from the sea beyond. When the taro was cooked Biria set it out and began to eat. She ate a good meal, for they planned on a long night of fishing, but Ingat was still talking, and she ate almost nothing, picking at the roots only and not doing more than taste them.

Biria finished the cooked taro, for she was a woman who hated waste, and then they were about to set out when Ingat had a new idea.

"Carry me," she said. "Carry me on your shoulders like a pickaninny." And Biria smiled, and Ingat climbed upon her shoulders and rode along the path.

Biria felt she was being foolish. She was a woman too old, she thought, for this kind of play; but as she went along she had the strange feeling that she was carrying her own child. She was happy in carrying Ingat. In a little while she took the cigarette from her mouth and passed it up to Ingat as mothers among her people have shared tobacco with their babies since time began. When Ingat played the naughty child and did not give it back Biria chuckled to herself and did not feel resentful.

"I am a fool," she thought, but she was not any the less happy.

And now Ingat had found the frogs in the billum net, and she began to eat them, and still Biria was happy, though Ingat could quite well have stayed her stomach earlier with the taro. But in the silence when Ingat was eating, Biria, trotting along the bush track with Ingat on her shoulders, heard again the thin sound of the sing-sing rising and falling on the evening air, for now it was very dark. She heard it; or she thought she heard it; she was not sure which.

And suddenly a new thought came to her that shocked the deeps of her mind; for she remembered how she had reckoned Ingat dead while she waited at the junction of the paths.

"This is no Ingat but a devil-woman," she thought. "Ingat is dead and a devil is using her body." And she had very great fear.

For it was a terrible thought. It was something beyond her consciousness and her experience, but Biria was a brave woman and she showed no sign. But she felt sure that the woman on her shoulders was a devil-woman, and she counted up the evidence:

The woman had eaten no taro, but only picked at it.

She had ridden on Biria's back and she had made it seem to Biria that she carried her own child.

She had taken Biria's cigarette and the frogs for Biria's family, and Biria had felt no resentment.

She had not heard the music of the sing-sing that Biria could hear, but had talked of other things.

Biria was sure now that this was a devil-woman who was luring her on through the deeper parts of the forest.

Before they could reach the sea they had to negotiate a thickness of trees that, for some forgotten reason, held a bad reputation. When Biria remembered that too, she stopped and said, "Let's rest awhile." She set Ingat down, or she set down the devil-woman that was Ingat, and then she made a little fire.

"We're making a fire already?" Ingat asked in surprise, and Biria answered, "I want to make bom-boms to light us through the black bush ahead."

Ingat laughed and sat herself down at the fire. So Biria brought palm fronds and made herself a torch.

She said, "While I have the torch I'll catch a couple of frogs to make up for the ones you ate. I promised Baisa to bring him a frog, for he loves them very much."

And Ingat answered, "We have the whole night, and there will be some time before the moon is up and we are ready to bom-bom the fish." She threw a little piece of wood on the fire and began to sing a happy little song to herself.

Biria took the torch and went up above the track and there she tied the torch upright above a little swampy place, with a vine to hold it to a tree stump. The place she chose caught the little breezes, and the torch swayed a fraction on its base, and the flame glowed and diminished and its light ebbed and swelled, so that Ingat, who could not see the torch, could nevertheless see the reflections of its light, and would believe Biria to be catching frogs.

But Biria was running, fleet and fast as a cassowary, running along the forest track as she had never run in her life, her unfettered breasts thudding against her chest, her thighs heedless of the little obstructions in her way. She ran and she ran until she came to her own village of Labu.

All of the people were in the village and she told them her story. She told them that Ingat, the lively one, the little Ingat, the beloved Ingat was dead, and that a devil-woman had taken her body. She told them that Ingat's village was wailing for her death, while Ingat's body walked the forest tracks. She told them how the devil-woman had tried to deceive her, to lure her into the dark thickness of bush on the way to the sea; how the devil-woman had used her and worked on her to make use of her in some unholy scheme.

Now Biria was not a woman given to imaginings. She was a housewife as dull of wit as any; and though her influence was not great, the tidings she brought were alarming. For there was little doubt but that the devil-woman, having marked Biria for her own, would come to claim her.

So the men of the village went to work. They built a huge fire and stacked it with the cooking stones they used to heat the ovens. And across the path leading to the village from the beach they dug a pit, deep and wide; and set men with bows guarding the path. They did all this with frantic haste, and when the stones were hot they took some and put them in the bottom of the pit and covered over the pit with a lacework of feeble sticks, and thus hid all their preparations beneath a cover of earth, very hastily fashioned, but nevertheless quite capable of deceiving an unwary eye. And then they waited, and heaped more wood on the fires, and set more bowmen round the path.

Now Ingat, while this had been going on, was sleepy by the fire. She waited a long time, singing a little song to herself. Once or twice she looked up and saw the torchlight glowing, ebbing and increasing among the trees, and she wished that Biria had not left her, for she was a woman who much liked company. By and by the vine holding the torch burned through, and the flame fell on the swampy mud beneath and was extinguished, and still Ingat waited by the fire for Biria to return, for she was a lazy woman.

A long time went by, and there was still no Biria, nor could Ingat hear any sign of her among the trees above the path. She called to her, and the forest was immediately silent, but still Biria did not reply. Ingat called and called. Then she made herself a torch of palm fronds and went to find her friend.

She searched a long time in the dark bush, but she found nothing, and all the time a fear grew on her, and her thoughts that were so happy became dark, and she was frightened. She came back to the fire and saw Biria's billum, with the spare lap-lap for swimming, and her lime-gourd for the chewing of betel, and her awls and her needles, and all the little things with which a woman would not willingly part. She took the billum in her hand and went back along the path to seek her friend, or to tell others that she had gone. She was little and bewildered, and she was caught with a dread of the night's events.

At the junction of the paths she hesitated, but her duty to Biria was clear, and she took the road that led to Labu.

Behind her the dark pursued, and the night that had at a stroke become so full of mystery, so empty of a friend; and when she was just a little way along the path she began to run, and fear ran behind her, and panic caught up with her, and she cried out, a fearsome lost cry that was of that night of fear; and so, running madly, she came upon the village of Labu, and the bowmen loosed their arrows, and in the same moment she fell into the pit upon the hot stones and was no more.

All the people of Labu came and piled the cooking stones from the fire upon her little body that was so light, so proper a vessel for her happiness; and she was baked like a pig in the oven until there was little left of her. In the morning the villagers of Labu took that little and buried it in a grave a long way from the village, and they planted bamboos on the grave. Only then were they satisfied, and they said, "The devil-woman is no more. She is dead truly."

Each man told the story of what they had seen. Englaf, an old man, said, "When she burst from the bush her face was full of hatred, and her belly was hot with anger against us all. And truly, if the woman Biria had not been wise, last night might have seen the end of everyone here."

"Truly her belly was hot against us all," they agreed; and they talked a great deal about the night, though there was little more they could say. And for the first time in her life, for she was a silent woman, Biria talked more than anyone.

"Her eyes flashed with hatred, and her mouth worked with anger, and she screamed at us all," she said. "But most of all her hatred was for me, this devil-woman. She hated me most because I tricked her with the torch to gain time for us, out there in the bush. And truly I was close to Death. I carried Death on my shoulders like a child."

But once, sitting quietly, she said, "It is sad about Ingat, for she was a happy woman and I was her friend. My heart was always turned to her. I was fond of her, and I used to do whatever she asked of me. It is sad about her. I will never have another friend like her."

The Beautiful
Pattern

THIS is a tale from long ago, of people removed a hundred generations and more from people who live today. Yet there is little changed in this land where the warm and living waters surge, swift and quiet, up the sloping beach and lap the piling of the houses at the height of the tide, and bare the jagged coral on the ebb. Hoada, the fisherman, still keeps his canoe by the palms near the creek in the place which seemed safe to Hoada his ancestor; and Aru, his wife, still daily sweeps the sand which is the garden of her home. The women take their green bananas to the sea to wash them for the cooking pots as they have done beyond the many many years of memory. The village, which has been a thousand villages in its materials and its workmanship, is still the same village; and the canoes and the houses and the cooking pots renewed are still the same. Even the broom with which Aru sweeps the sand clear of the litter of her pigs and her hens is still the same broom, fashioned from the dead flower of the dying sago palm, and bound precisely as was the broom that rotted and fell to pieces a hundred generations ago.

Only Mala is no more. And that is good, even though he was so handsome, so strong, so gay, so light of skin. For men hated him as

they watched him stroll the earth in his disdain, flicking the raindrops from his hair with a two-pronged comb, spitting his buwo
contemptuously on the ground, settling his dagger-bracelet firm on
his arm muscles; and it is not good for men to hate. Nor was it
good for them that the women should adore Mala, that the earth
and the air and the trees and the birds should obey him; that the
light and the dark should come at his command.

And yet it is bad that Mala is no more, for he was mischievous
and loved a joke; and that is good for men. For he was strong and
handsome, and that is an example for them. And he was clever and
a great artist, and that is an inspiration forever. And it is sad that
there are no more demigods to strut the earth and make men sharpen
their wits and flex their muscles. Mala is gone indeed, and all that
remains of him is the beautiful pattern.

The pattern is gone now from the arrowheads of Mala, and you
will search for it in vain among the carvings of the great piles which
support the council house. Yet in those drowsy islands it is never
forgotten, nor ever will be as long as Mala is remembered, for every
woman carries it on her body, tattooed lightly yet boldly into the
secrecy of the soft skin between her thighs. So if you would share
the secret of the pattern you must share more than the secret, and
that is your responsibility and your choice. It is a very beautiful
pattern. The reason for the pattern is the story of Mala and the
fisherman's wife, and this is that story.

Aru, the wife of Hoada, the fisherman, was sweeping the sand
about her house and carrying away the rubbish on a taro leaf when
an arrow glanced from the trunk of a coconut palm above her head
and dropped to the ground at her feet. It was not an arrow such as
the hunters of the village used, with a reed shaft and a head of the
tough limbom palm. It was a golden arrow, craftily fashioned, lightly
balanced. Its hardwood head was carved in multiple barbs alter-
nating from one side to another like thorns on a branch, each barb

hooked and curved and savagely beautiful. Beneath the head, a light tassel adorned the shaft of golden cane, and all its length the shaft was carved with a beautiful pattern.

Aru picked up the arrow and held it in her hands, and caught her breath with the beauty of the pattern. Then she climbed the ladder of her house and hid the arrow and returned swiftly to the open clearing and picked up her broom.

In a little while the bushes parted and a man walked into the clearing, a man of the hills with a big chest and heavy thighs, yet slim and evenly muscled, and light skinned and handsome. He stood there for a moment looking about him, facing the woman, but taking no notice of her. Then he drew the comb from his hair and dressed his head with it. In that still, warm clearing, Aru could hear the comb's two teeth making little noises as they flicked through the thick, lime-bleached hair, noises like the tiny clap of two leaves of a palm frond in the wind, like a fraction of the surge of the surf upon the sand.

The stranger combed his hair and watched the woman. She was still young and beautiful. It was ten years since she had given birth to her eldest son, but her breasts were firm for a matron's, and her skin was fresh and golden. Below her waist she wore a bright new skirt, corn-yellow and smoky-rose and brown and mud-gray in a bold design of silky threads. Across her back her father, when she was young, had tattooed the record of his voyagings, that her husband might remember and prove himself no less adventurous. Over her breasts and deep below her armpits were records of the heads he had taken, that her own men might prove as brave. The tattoo patterns were light and graceful.

In her hair she wore a flower of the wild hibiscus, and its yellow delicacy enhanced the strength of her straight-boned features. She was good to look at, and the stranger put his comb away and spat his buwo on the sand, the betel-reddened saliva streaking the sand's white. Then he settled his dagger-bracelets higher on his arm muscles and walked across the clearing to Aru. He said, "I am looking for my arrow."

Aru said nothing.

He said, more directly, "Have you seen an arrow?"

Aru answered, "No."

Then the stranger came very close and put his mouth to her ear and said, "I am Mala," and Aru knew the things that were in his mind. She knew there was nothing she could keep from Mala, for the earth and the sea would open a way for him. She knew that the shinguards of bark which ornamented his legs could carry him as swiftly as the day's first gleam of sunshine over the hills. And she was beginning to know that women were pliant as the water when Mala looked at them.

She said, "Perhaps I could find your arrow, but I would like to keep the beautiful pattern."

Mala answered, "Give me the arrow, and you shall have the pattern for as long as you live."

So Aru walked into the house and took the arrow from its hiding place in the thatch of sago leaves, and brought it to Mala. And Mala took her by a forest path to a bend in the creek at the back of the hill behind the village. Here there was a grassy patch, and here he laid Aru down, and took his tattooing needles made from the bones of the flying fox, and tattooed the beautiful pattern at the most secret height of her thigh.

And when the pattern was completed he rubbed the wounds with galpandot, the magic sap of a shrub which tinctured the wounds with the sea-blue which, of all shades, is the most desirable for a skin tattoo; and then he wiped away the blood with a taro leaf, and this taro leaf he threw into the water of the stream. Then he stood back and he looked at Aru, the wife of Hoada, the fisherman, as she lay there on the ground, and he combed his hair and he spat his buwo and he joggled the pas-pas bracelets on his arms.

Now all this time Hoada, the fisherman, and his two sons, Aros who was ten years old and Tofilau who was two years younger, had been fishing on the reef. It was a good day, but the fish were not biting. Nevertheless each of the three had had some little luck and there were a few glistening bodies lying on the platform of the canoe; not many, and those not large. Toward the end of the day Hoada saw, not very far away from him, a huge crowd of birds working the water, wheeling and diving and feeding on a mighty school of little creatures that the big fish on the bottom of the sea had frightened to the surface.

So Hoada and his sons quickly lifted the stone anchor from its niche in the reef and hauled in the long rope they had made from the roots of the pandanus palm, and paddled quickly over to the school, for it was not far away and there was no time to set the sail. As soon as he had paid out his line, Tofilau pulled a fish, and Aros immediately after him, but Hoada's line lay slack in the water. These fish were big and they were feeding hungrily, and Tofilau and Aros began to pull them in as quickly as they could handle them, but Hoada had no luck. He changed his baits and he weighted his sinkers, and after awhile he took a new line, but the fish would not touch his hook. Then he tied a scrap of bark from the tanket plant above the bone hook for a charm; but still his luck would not change.

In the meantime the boys were filling the canoe with their fish. The water was lapping the gunwales with the weight of the catch when Hoada at long last felt a little movement on his hook and pulled in his line. But there was no fish there. Instead, there was a taro leaf, green and fresh from the lily, and on the taro leaf a smear of blood.

"What does this mean?" cried Hoada. "Why the leaf? And why

the blood? Is it bird's blood? Is it pig's blood? Man's blood?" And then in a terrible voice he cried, "It is woman's blood." And he cried, "Pull up the anchor. Be quick, and let us go."

And a breeze sprang up, and with their canoe filled full of fish they sailed for the village. When they cleared the reef in the bay, the boys would have sailed the canoe onto the beach as usual, but Hoada stopped them and they dropped the anchor in four feet of water, just past the rising swell that surged back gently from the sloping beach. Hoada took the conch shell from its place on the platform and called the village, and the people came running down to the beach to share in the miraculous catch; and when they saw the canoe in the water they ran in laughing and calling; the men and the women and the children together, frolicking in the surf, happy to get the good fish.

Aru, the wife of Hoada, came down to the beach, but stayed short of the water, and Hoada called to her to come and get the fish. She shook her head. She said she was wearing a new pul-pul, and he could see that this was so, for the skirt was very bright and silky. But he called to her just the same, and this time his voice threatened, so that she came to the canoe. But when she was wet nearly to the hips a wave lifted the pul-pul and Hoada saw the new tattoo between her thighs.

Until that day such a thing had not been seen in those islands.

It happened that at this time the village was preparing to erect a new council house, and the elders of the village sent out invitations to all the famous men thereabouts to come, so that each of them might carve a tree trunk to contribute to the building. The tree trunks lay ready in the pulat, the sacred enclosure wherein no woman might walk. When a woman defied the ban—and in every generation there was one who did—she disappeared from the face of the earth; and the women who lived accepted the inevitable and stayed away. So that none of them knew of the patterns which the tree trunks were taking in the pulat, nor were they told the identity of the carvers.

Invitations had gone to the luluai, the chief, and to the luluai of the village in the hills; one to this man who was a great fisherman, and one to a man skilled in the building of canoes; one to a sorcerer who could kill with a look, and some to others who were admired of the people. And all these men worked in the pulat, carving the great piles for the council house. And one invitation had gone to Mala, and he carved more dexterously than all the rest. As his pattern emerged from the wood the men could see that it was more beautiful than the others, and Hoada, the fisherman, knew where he had seen its like.

For it was the pattern of the golden arrow, and the pattern that was the secret of Aru, his wife.

So Hoada talked with the men of the village, and took them into his confidence, and they agreed upon a plan. And when the carvings, after many months, were ready and the holes dug for the piles and only the building waited, they asked Mala to go into the hole and direct the placing of the first pile. To this Mala agreed, but before he climbed down into the hole he went apart into the forest, taking half a coconut shell with him.

He filled the shell with the juice of the bena-bena plant, which flows a brilliant red, and he covered it with slats of dead bamboo, and he placed it all on top of his skull and carefully covered it with the thick luxuriance of his mop of lime-bleached hair.

Then he came back to the clearing, looking insolently at the men about him, and he flicked the comb through his hair a couple of times while they waited, and he spat his buwo and joggled the pas-pas bracelets on his arms until Hoada asked politely whether he would kindly step into the hole to direct the placing of the timber. And at that Mala climbed down into the deep hole.

At this moment the men standing by let go the great carved tree trunk, and it crashed down on top of Mala. The men saw the blood splash wide, and they heard the crunch of bones, and they held the pile upright and filled in the hole truly, with great rejoicing, because a council house set upon such a foundation would bring a wealth of good qualities to the initiates who came to their manhood there.

A man cannot leave a good thing alone; and months later Hoada, the fisherman, walked to the top of the hill to the village whence came Mala. Perhaps Hoada went to jeer; perhaps to clear up certain suspicions in his mind. When he came to the village he met a man by the track and asked him, "What of Mala?"

The man said, "He is in the house by the peak. He went by here a little while ago, having watched you come up the track; and he was laughing. He's waiting for you by his house."

When Hoada went a little farther into the village clearing he saw that the man had not lied. For Mala stood by the doorway of his house flicking the raindrops from his hair with the prongs of his comb. And as Hoada watched him he put away the comb, and spat his betel nut and joggled the pas-pas bracelets on his arms, and greeted him quite cordially.

Of this part of the story there is no explanation except that the blood which stained the post carved with the beautiful pattern was the brilliant red juice of the bena-bena, and the crunching of bones was the breaking of bamboo strips, and it is well known that Mala had power over the earth to make it open a way for him.

And perhaps it is not true that there is no more Mala. Perhaps Mala is always and everywhere, and some husbands have always thought so. In those islands lapped forever by the warm waters the women believe that while they carry the beautiful pattern secretly in the soft skin of their thighs, some part of Mala will never die.

The Vision
at the Spring

I N the evening's cool, in the freshness after the
storm, the piping of the flutes sang to the high
mountains like the chiming of bells. The two
notes were tenuous yet penetrating, a gentle shivering of the silence
that ruled the steep cliffs and the chasms of the narrow valleys; a
sound to which the ear was so attuned that though it was less than
the unnoticed calling of the birds, it claimed the brain insistently.
Its song was the song of sadness, of frustration; of lost hearts and
discovered sorrows. In the two notes of the flutes were the monotony
of forever, the fleetingness of the passing moment; the beauty of
things unborn, the sweetness of memory. In the village of Daua,
sang the flutes; the young men and the young women were preparing for a dance.

From the village of Ikidi two young men set out lightheartedly.
To the frustrations of the dance, to the sorrows of the kanana they
brought skins glowing with the sheen of oil from the nuts of the
mountain pandanus, and faces that were painted with red and yellow and white, and arms decorated with the blue wings of birds,
pinned into woven bracelets of cured grasses. They had taken a
careful day to dress for the beautiful girls of Daua.

Gorunubi, who was the senior by a year, wore on his head a wide circlet like a crown, studded with the shells of the small cowries that had come from an unknown coast in the swift exchanges of trade. It was topped with a red rosette of parrot feathers surrounded by sheaves of plumes from the white cockatoo; and behind this diadem, and soaring half the height of a man above his head, six birds of paradise, sun-dried, were thrust by the beaks into his hair, so that their wings and tails fanned out into a crest of red and gold magnificence. From his neck was suspended a gold-lip pearl shell a foot across, and gleaming slivers of the nacreous shell of the green sea snail were fastened into his headband so that they covered his ears. He wore a half-moon of the green sea snail in his nose. His belt, a hand-span deep, was embossed with raised designs, and from it his billum swung to the ground in front, and the peace plant he wore behind was flanked with tails of amber palm nuts. He wore the fur of a tree-climbing kangaroo twisted about his right arm, and he swaggered as he walked.

Kobuludumana was not so handsome as Gorunubi, a little less assured, a little less tall, and he walked without a swagger. Yet he was a hunter to be admired, for he wore ten birds of paradise in his hair, clasped behind a yellow-straw circlet in which iridescent green beetles, thumb-sized, were imprisoned fast in a pattern of light. He wore a gold-lip shell on his forehead and his chin, as well as one suspended from his neck, and the fur about his right arm was more golden than Gorunubi's. His muscles swelled beneath the bracelets on his upper arms.

Each carried a warrior's spear as they walked the mountain paths alongside the Wahgi River that runs between Ikidi and Daua, but their arming was for the campaigns of love and not the field of war.

All the world of youth waited at the long thatched house in Daua for the kanana to begin. The girls sat close about the fires in the smoke-filled hall; for the mountain air was sharp; the drummers took their places at the door, and the men filed in for the dance, stooping low so that the great plumes nodding on their heads should not break against the roof. When the drums began to throb they danced, swaying and singing to the rhythm of the beats, losing themselves in the sad ecstasy of the dance.

"What shall we do then?" sang the dancers.

"What shall we do in the morning when the sun is high?
Shall we go down to the cedar by the swamp,
The tree where the water bursts from the roots in a stream?
But the spring by the tree is dry and is gone forever,
So we shall go to the market and barter for paint,
For red paint and yellow to paint on the skin of our faces."

The music rose and swelled, and the glistening bodies leaned closer and ever closer till the bones in the noses clashed one against the other, and the singing died away, and the swaying lessened, and the dancers swung silently, each one lone in the crowd.

And here again there was a difference between the two young men of Ikidi, for while Gorunubi sat properly, erect and distant, and waited for the girls on either hand to make their choice of him, Kobuludumana, the younger man, was quick to choose the prettiest, and when the men moved on in a chain he changed his place to be with the girl of his choice; and if the girls sighed with awe as they watched the proud and distant Gorunubi, they giggled when Kobuludumana came within their orbit, and over-reached themselves a little, and cheated on the rules of the dance to claim him for partner.

"The paints for our faces are sold from the market place,
The stalls are empty and the buyers gone to their homes.

*We are left with our wares, and no paint for the skin of
our faces,
Nothing to deck us in color when dancing begins.
Now we will go to the spring at the foot of the cedar,
The tree where the water bursts from the roots in a stream."*

The dancers sang on and on, weaving their dreams. And some
under cover of the singing made arrangements to meet the girls of
Daua, whispering the things they could not say in the village. And
in the long and smoke-filled house many men charted the voyage of
their future.

But Gorunubi and Kobuludumana danced till the morning light
stole in at the narrow doorway to contest the rosy glow of the fires,
and then set out to follow the winding track through the mountains
to Ikidi.

They carried stalks of tanket, the peace plant, in their hands, and
as they walked through the shoulder-high fields of kunai grass they
beat on the grass with the tanket leaves, so that the dew was shaken
to the ground. At Kiliman they came to the roaring rapids of the
Wahgi River, tumbling down from mountains that pierced the frozen
sky to join the wild Pareri and finally the sea; but, here, quiet for a
little stretch and spread out wide so that there was a crossing. They
waded the Wahgi and continued on by the upriver trail until they
came to the outer hunting grounds of Ikidi and climbed the little
mountain that sits in the way.

Halfway to the top of the mountain they stopped and rested, for
they were tired with the night of dancing, and the sun was halfway
to its zenith and probing the very deepest valleys with its rays, and
the morning clouds had dissipated their substance altogether.

Now when they stopped they looked about them as men will, and
on the other side of the Wahgi they saw two girls dancing on a rock.
The rock was a little below them, but the chasm through which the
river ran was so deep and narrow that the girls were close, and the

strong light of midmorning made them seem closer still. Gorunubi
and Kobuludumana had left beautiful girls behind them at the dance,
but the beauty of these two who danced upon the rock surpassed that
of anyone they had ever seen. The girls were tall and straight, and
their skins dark and glowing. Their shoulders were smooth and their
necks held high, and their full breasts issued evenly and smoothly
from their bodies that moved in grace.

They were dressed in the Chimbu fashion, and their sleek light
pul-puls swung from their belts, and swayed and clung to their
lissome thighs as they danced upon the rock. The gold-lip shells
about their necks threw great rainbows of light across the chasm
into the eyes of the youths from Ikidi, and it seemed to them also
that the girls themselves possessed a radiance like the morning light
imprisoned in a dewdrop, a radiance that splintered the air into a
dazzle and made even the surface of the rock on which they danced
sparkle and shine like the wet plumage of a river bird.

The men called to the girls, but the girls danced on, and took no
notice. They did not even look and giggle; they just danced together
on top of the rock, their arms about each other's shoulders, cheek
touching cheek, breast touching breast, and thigh touching thigh.
Kobuludumana raced away down the mountainside to the waters of
the Wahgi and flung himself into the boiling river. Breasting the
rapids, treading the treacherous rolling boulders he crossed to the
farther bank and began to climb. When he came in sight of the rock
he stopped.

The rock was there, a great outcrop such as you might find on
any hill; but the girls had gone.

"Where are they? Which way did they go?" Kobuludumana
called to Gorunubi.

"What do you mean? They stand in front of you," Gorunubi
answered. "Open your eyes wider, blind man. Open your eyes."

The rock was there, with a shelf near the top where it sprang from and made one with the green grass of the hill; and this was the shelf on which the girls had danced, but there was no one and nothing on the rock.

He climbed a little farther, and he could see all the hill thereabouts, but the girls had gone.

"Where are they?" he called again, and Gorunubi waved impatiently. He didn't answer Kobuludumana, but called to the girls as though they were still there.

"We are the men of Ikidi," he called. "We are the chosen of Ikidi who have taken greetings to the people of Daua and are now returning."

Kobuludumana climbed up and up until he stood upon the rock where the girls had danced. He faced Gorunubi across the valley and called to him.

"Which way did they go?" he asked again.

"Talk to them, man," Gorunubi called back impatiently. "You are with them. Talk to them."

Kobuludumana looked about him in bewilderment, and with an expression of impatience Gorunubi hastened down from the opposite hill and he, too, crossed the Wahgi and climbed to the rock. And he, too, when he saw Kobuludumana alone said, "Which way did they go?"

They looked everywhere. They combed the hill and went down to search in the valley near the spur. They examined the rocky ground for tracks but they found nothing. They climbed up and across and about the mountain until their throats were dry.

Now they saw that from the stone there issued a trickle of water, and it flowed in a deep crevice across the shelf of rock where the girls had danced. There was only a little water in the depths of the crevice, and it poured itself away again among the rocks without coming to the surface; but it was flowing water and it came from a substantial spring.

So Kobuludumana took a leaf of the wild sugar cane growing near by, and fashioned it into a cup, and dipped water from the crevice and offered it to Gorunubi. Gorunubi tasted, and looked at Kobuludumana; then he drained the cup. He licked his lips. "That's not ordinary water," he said. "That's water of another kind." He filled the cup and handed it to his friend. "It's wonderful water. Not the kind of water we have always drunk. Much better than the water we know," he said. "Its taste is altogether different."

Kobuludumana tried the water on his tongue and the flavor was a flavor he had never known, sharp and full and satisfying; not sweet, like the sap of the sugar, not acid like the juice of the orange. There was a quality in it like the satisfaction of new meat; and his body thirsted for it. Yet he and Gorunubi soon came to their fill of the miraculous water. They went then to the valley, and cut lengths of the giant bamboo and made water carriers, and cupped the water into the carriers with folded cane leaves, and carried them back to Ikidi.

When they came up near the village they began calling from a long way off, in the high, throat-easing ululation, the language without consonants which the mountain man assumes when his hearers are at a distance. They called, "Come and try the water. Come and drink this water that is like no other." And everyone came, the old men and the chiefs, and the young men and the boys, and everyone sipped of the water in the bamboos and they said, "True, this water is better than the water we know. This water is a good water, and this is a great find." Their bodies were grateful for the qualities they found in the water; and to the new flavor, the taste that made this water different from all others, they gave the name of salt.

Then everyone killed pigs, and they killed their roosters for a feast, and they brought all the produce of the gardens and prepared a great celebration with everything that everyone could bring, and they listened to the tale of the beautiful maidens who had shown the spring and the rock to the young men Gorunubi and Kobuludumana. To the feast they invited the people from the village of Gunagl, and it was the greatest feast in those parts, all because of the water that came up in the stone on the mountain above the Wahgi River between Kiliman and Ikidi.

Only Kobuludumana, looking at the girls of his village, was discontented, for their skins were dull compared with the shining skins of the girls at the spring; and their bodies under-developed, and their eyes less sparkling, though they had seemed well enough before.

But in the counting up, surely no feast had ever been better advised. For after the discovery of the spring the village prospered and the people grew healthy. They used the salt water from the spring in their cooking because they found that it imparted its satisfactions to the food; but for drinking returned to the water of the streams as they had done before. They talked much about the girls that Kobuludumana and Gorunubi had seen, and some said it was a vision conjured up by the morning sun dancing on the rock.

Kobuludumana went often and sat on the mountain across the river in the mornings, and looked for the maidens to appear again, because this vision had brought to him a beauty such as he would not have formerly believed possible. But the maidens never came. He sat and watched the lines of women with their bamboos carrying the water from the spring, but none of them had the grace, or the shape, or the beauty of the girls who had danced here on the morning after the kanana at Daua.

The old men and the chiefs often went to look at the spring, and they talked of putting the village there, but it was not in a good defensive position, and it was too far from garden land, and they could not risk the change. And with the wealth of the salt, which made all things better to eat, came disasters. For enemies watched, and preyed on the women who went daily to the spring, and they took many heads, and the people of Ikidi mourned because of the killing of their women. And they set guards about the spring when the women used it; but these men, standing on guard, lost much time from other work, and the village threatened to become poor, because of its new wealth.

They tried to store the water, but when it had stood a day or two in the containers, the smell of it became a pestilence, and the water bitter and black and rank, and the containers took the taste and the smell to themselves, so that thereafter their usefulness was at an end. The salt in the water was good, but the stinking pestilence that accompanied it grew with keeping, and supplies had to be brought fresh each day from the spring.

Kobuludumana said to Sigiba, the chief, "If we take the salt out of the water, then we can store the salt, and in a little time we will get enough salt from the spring to last a year, and the women will not have to leave the village of Ikidi once every morning, and the men can hunt and the women work the gardens."

"True," said Sigiba, the chief. "If the salt in the water were a dead stick that a man could pluck out with his fingers, we could take the salt from the water, and keep it separate; and the rest would follow as you foretell. But how can a man take the salt from the water, the salt that is one with the water, and a part of it?"

Kobuludumana took a cup folded from a leaf of sugar cane and dipped it in the water and unfolded the cup and dried the leaf in the sun. Then he put his tongue to the leaf and tasted the salt upon it, and gave the leaf to Sigiba, who tasted it likewise and passed it to the old men, and they also tasted the salt upon the leaf though it was dry. So they learned from Kobuludumana that there could be salt without water.

Then Kobuludumana wet another leaf in the spring and dried it in the sun and burned the leaf in a little fire, and the ashes of the leaf were salty. For many days he burned one leaf after another, using the leaves of many plants that grew in quantity, and he found the leaf that made the least ash.

It was the blade of the kangaroo grass that grows in profusion upon the bare spurs of the mountains above the Wahgi Valley. So in the season when the grass was ripe and dry the people of Ikidi cut it in great quantities and carried it to the spring, and made a trough in the rock, and soaked up all the water in the trough with the grass, and carried the grass to a place near by and set it to dry in the sun. And when there was a heap of grass bigger than the houses in the village of Ikidi they set fire to it, a little at a time, so that it burned always in the one place, and the burning of the grass took half a month.

Then the people took the ashes of the grass and put them into wooden troughs; and they cut away the fibre that guards new leaves in the growth of young palms, and set this matted fiber at the ends of the troughs for strainers; and they dripped water on the ashes, and the water dripped from the troughs through the strainers thick and greasy with the salt it carried.

This water they dried on the hot flat rocks, and it left the salt behind it. They learned to hasten the drying by setting a flat rock above a slow fire and making a mold for salt upon it; and there was a sufficiency of salt to last the village all the year.

Now the people of Ikidi and the people of Gunagl both harvested the salt from the spring, and the villages grew rich. From all up and down the district of the Chimbu, and farther into the utmost recesses of the Wahgi Valley, the people came twice a year into the places set apart for trading, and there they met in a brief peace. After the time of the first leaf burning, the people of Ikidi and Gunagl brought baskets of salt to the trading, and measured out the salt, and became rich in axes and pots and pigs, in dried birds of paradise, in gold-lip shell and sea snail, in lizard skins for drums, and in all kinds of wealth. The men of Ikidi paid a high bride-price for many women, and the villages grew and prospered.

Seeing this, when the season for trading had passed, the tribesmen on the hills raided the villages of Ikidi and Gunagl, and they fought many wars, and lost many heads. The chosen time for the raids was when the men were on the mountain spurs gathering the grass for soaking, and when the salt was drying on the flat rock platforms near the spring.

And the old men and the chiefs said, "If we had the salted grass on the Ikidi side of the Wahgi, then we could make our salt in peace, and defend ourselves," for the spurs and the platforms, like the spring itself, were in a bad defensive position and open to attack from the hills above.

Yet no one could swim the river with the grass and keep it from the river water, which would rob it of its salt.

Kobuludumana thought much about this problem, especially when he sat on the mountain across the Wahgi from the spring, and looked in vain to see the maidens of his vision.

One day as he sat there he saw a spider, which in the Chimbu they call Gongabae, spinning its web in the branches of a tree. It was a large spider and the web was strong, and Kobuludumana watched it as it traveled its road of silk from a branch to the trunk. It ran backward and forward, and it strengthened the first line it cast with stays of web, and soon it began to make the net.

Kobuludumana watched it and he thought, and from the spider he took the idea of throwing a line across the river. So he called the people of the village together, Sigiba, the chief, and the old men, and they gathered long lengths of cane from the bush, and made ropes of roots and fiber such as they used to lash together the frames of houses, and strong bamboos, and lengths of timber of sorts that he thought would be suitable. And high above the waters of the Wahgi they carried a line across the river.

They worked backward and forward on the line, and strengthened it and stayed it back to the trees on the cliff; and set other lines above to give a handgrip, and widened the footway so that a man could walk across with ease, carrying the salted grass upon his back. And this was the first bridge ever seen, and Kobuludumana the first bridgebuilder. Yet Gongabae, the spider, built a bridge before Kobuludumana.

And now the people of Ikidi and of Gunagl harvested the kangaroo grass and steeped it in the spring, and carried it to the safe side of the Wahgi River, and there they made the salt and dried it on a flat rock near the villages. Here they were well guarded, and enemies could approach them only from below; and the raids grew fewer and the villages prospered.

In this year, Kobuludumana was an aging man, and the things he saw in the village seemed to him not so good as the things that were there in his youth. He never saw any of the village maidens so beautiful as the two who danced by the spring, yet it was forced on him that the children and the youths were better and stronger and handsomer than those who had danced that night in the kanana at Daua. This was truly so, for the salt had brought them health and built up their bodies, and the riches the salt brought insured that they fed well and often. Indeed, the people of the Chimbu had become known among the mountain people for their beauty.

They were also strong, and in the seasons when they risked themselves on the side of the river where the spring lay, they were well guarded. But their method of taking the salt from the spring became known, and sometimes they found that others had used the water before them, and cut the grass, and they had to wait until the supply built up; for there was little enough water in the spring for their purpose, though it was rich with salt.

The old men came often to Kobuludumana with this problem,

and he thought of it often as he sat on the hill and watched for the maidens who never came back.

One day he came to the village and he said:

"I have been watching for many years, and now I am sure. There is a snake which guards the water in the stone. His name is Nalanae and his house is in the rock itself. His skin is half white and half red, and his tail is like enough to his head, so that he can strike and kill from any direction. And there are all manner of taboos which govern the taking of the salt, and Nalanae is their guardian."

They heard him, and though they had never doubted that the maidens at the spring were a vision, they nevertheless believed in the actual existence of Nalanae. And thereafter they followed exactly the taboos that the old men put on the taking of the salt. In the following season, before the taking of the salt began, many people, some from Ikidi and some from elsewhere, were found dead near the spring on the mountainside; and the people of Ikidi and Gunagl knew that they died because of the breaking of the taboos and the great jealousy of Nalanae; and in the trading season they told the people of other tribes that this was so. But among the old men, some knew truly the manner of the deaths.

In this way the taking of the salt was left to the proper season for the grass, under the proper conditions, and though there were wars and raids, the people of the upper Chimbu and particularly of Ikidi and Gunagl governed the harvest of the salt.

Kobuludumana lived a long time, and he was honored when he died. He lived to see the daughters of Ikidi grow nearly, but not quite, as beautiful as the women by the spring; but as he grew old he clung more and more to his seat on the mountainside above the bridge he had cast across the waters of the Wahgi.

To this day the serpent Nalanae watches the spring from his house in the rock, and the white feathers of cockatoos and the red birds of paradise are taboos belonging to him.

And the bridge still spans the chasm. It has been renewed and strengthened in every year, but it is still the same bridge and if you ask the people they will tell you it is the bridge of Kobuludumana.

"Kobuludumana built the bridge," they say. "And this was the same Kobuludumana who saw the vision of the women at the salt spring."

For it is true in the Chimbu, and perhaps elsewhere, that it is a man's visions, and not his deeds, that make him live forever.

The Impact

*T*HE early European explorers paid but little attention to New Guinea and made as little impact. In scattered areas throughout the country and its outlying islands there are indications that actual colonization attempts may have briefly succeeded—a chain of buildings in the Trobriand Group, and in Woodlark Island, far to the east, for example—but of these early arrivals there is no European record, and the native legends and the stories which represent the communal memory do not recognize them.

Our record begins with D'Abreu, who sighted New Guinea in 1511. De Menezes visited it in 1526, Alvaro de Saavedra in 1528, and Ortiz de Retez named it in 1546, supposing a resemblance between its natives and those he had seen on the Guinea Coast in Africa.

The explorers followed on through the centuries—Torres, D'Entrecasteaux, a long list of names; but the reports they brought back, even when glowing, did not encourage settlement. In 1793 the British East India Company briefly occupied a base in the west, but soon withdrew. The Dutch laid claim to the sultanate of Tidor, a Malayan empire which included but did not utilize several tracts of land in New Guinea. In 1841 the British Government admitted these claims and in 1848 the Dutch proclaimed sovereignty over the western half of the island, an area of 150,000 square miles.

Until about 1875 these and other brief European contacts with New Guinea all seemed designed to leave a lasting heritage of hatred with the natives, normally a kind and friendly people at first meeting. Early explorers of all the European nations shot and blasted their way through barricades of living flesh, and of themselves created a hostility to the stranger. James Cook, the Great Navigator, was one of the most humane of the explorers, yet, in a single month, from the seventh of October, 1769, he or his crew members shot nearly a score of people, sometimes by way of enforcing trading conditions and sometimes from sheer curiosity. Other explorers were less considerate.

But this was nothing compared with events of the first half of the Nineteenth Century. Sydney and San Francisco had become the haunts of wild adventurers; and sandalwood and slaves the lures which spread these adventurers sporadically over the wild Pacific. Sandalwood was discovered in Fiji about 1805; or, rather, in that year its trade potentialities were recognized; and the sandalwooders ventured everywhere. Thirty or forty years later there was a huge unsatisfied demand for labor to work the sugar plantations of northern Australia; and the blackbirders went out from Sydney, in every hull that could carry sail, to fill their holds with protesting humanity. They shot down their opposition, and they were not policed. In these years neither Britain nor any other European nation was concerned with acquisition of territory in the Pacific. New Guinea and New Zealand were without authority and without law, and refugees from the law elsewhere were safe upon their coasts.

In 1840 the British, under protest, but driven by the representation of Edward Gibbon Wakefield and the competition of the French, annexed New Zealand, and for the hardy, free-roving criminals of the day, New Guinea remained the only sizable refuge in the Pacific. They made full use of it.

By 1875 the Anti-Slavery Society was urging the occupation of New Guinea by Britain, believing that the establishment of law would be a curb on some of the excesses committed, excesses which the natives, when they were able, as often as not repaid in kind. Britain did not listen to the society's representations, but for reasons of their own the Australian colonies did, and added their voices to the plea. For Queensland, the most northern state, separated from New Guinea by only eighty miles of shallow, reef-studded water, the acquisition of New Guinea (or that portion of it that was not already claimed by Holland) meant a supply of cheap labor for the plantations; for Victoria and New South Wales, the other two colonies interested, it meant a defense bulwark erected along the vulnerable north coast of the country; and for all three it meant a lessening of the general lawlessness of the Pacific.

The Governor of Queensland, in 1883, commissioned a police magistrate named Chester to annex New Guinea in the name of Great Britain. The Mother Country, heavily preoccupied with Indian affairs, repudiated the gesture; but, her hand thus forced, in the following year commissioned Commodore Erskine to declare a protectorate over the southern half of the unoccupied area. She also indicated that she would take over the rest at a later date in a "hands off" proclamation to other European powers, but Bismarck took up the challenge. On the sixth of November, 1884, the British protectorate was proclaimed; on the sixteenth of the same month Germany took over the remainder of the island.

Britain called the tune and Australia paid the piper. Britain appointed a special commissioner, Sir Peter Scratchley, who died shortly after his arrival in New Guinea. Three years later Britain delegated responsibility to Queensland, Victoria and New South Wales; and on the federation of the Australian colonies, about 1900, Australia assumed it. After the First World War the Ger-

man colony (which, by the way, had been developed in smaller area but much more intensively) was mandated to Australia, and from then on the two were administered together.

Throughout the long period of lawlessness there were special conditions in New Guinea which prevented the people from rising as one and throwing off the invaders. The first of these special conditions arose from the fact that each tribe was inimical to its neighbor. The language barrier was a most important problem; a secondary one was the difficulty of intercommunication. Even today there are few roads in New Guinea. Ships and aircraft provide nearly all the transport. In earlier days, the sea routes, for canoes that could only be used before the wind, were in practice limited to the seasons when the trade winds changed—in general, two short periods in every year. By long custom these periods were set apart for the occasions of peace and trading expeditions were then organized. Major-General Sir Peter Scratchley, Her Majesty's first Special Commissioner for New Guinea, arrived on the occasion of one of these trading truces, and he watched the big canoes sailing about the bay in preparation for departure, girls with interlaced arms dancing upon the bows, shifting their bodies about with a continuous swing which sent their grass skirts swirling like those of a ballet dancer. He estimated that from a small group of villages the trading canoes took westward thirty thousand large clay pots over a route of two hundred miles, bringing back in exchange 150 tons of sago, after paying for food en route with both pots and sago.

But the average tribesman in the average tribe had no contact except the brief impacts of aggression with other people.

In these circumstances the imposition of an alien authority was simplified but, with lack of understanding and exploratory investigation, absurd mistakes were made. The first expedition landed on the coast of the best available harbor at Port Moresby, and Sir Peter Scratchley and Commander Erskine appointed the chief of the nearest village as a kind of potentate. *The chief was Boevagi, head of the Motu seafaring village of which the scanty holdings were maintained by the benevolence of the Koiari, a rather fiercer people who inhabited the hills beyond, and whose indifferent friendship gave the Motu a little indifferent protection.* Sir Peter's first action was to summon twenty-five chiefs to the ceremony of declaring the protectorate and advising twenty-four of them to "look up to Bow Vagi [sic] as their head and to refer to him in all cases requiring arbitration." At a later date the administration also imposed a bastard version of the Motu language upon all the people of Australian New Guinea as the official language of the country.

To show his authority Boevagi was given "an ebony stick having a florin let into its head as a mark of authority and was also invested with a cast-off Commodore's coat, cocked hat and trousers. Either no boots were given him or they had been lost. As he did not consider himself properly dressed without boots he threw out strong hints to Sir Peter Scratchley that he would like a pair, but unfortunately no one had any to spare. . . . Sir Peter made him a present of some red cloth, tobacco and a tomahawk."

Having little respect for Boevagi, the other chiefs conceived somewhat less for the authority he was said to represent.

The first Australian Governor, Sir William MacGregor, enforced his authority with guns. He was a big man and a bully, and he hammered the undersized natives considerably. But he was just, if hard, and under him the country was developed although the expenditure allowed him and his successors was amazingly meager. He did also establish a native constabulary in place of the English military bodyguard which had served Sir Peter, and while the train-

ing of this constabulary varied according to the temperament of the officer in charge of each isolated squad, it was eventually forged into a splendid instrument of development.

This was the responsibility of Sir Hubert Murray who had been in office some dozen years when German New Guinea was added to his charge. Sir Hubert, a heavyweight boxing champion of the British Empire and a legislator of no mean ability, befriended the natives, established small co-operative industries and encouraged plantations, frowned on the needless killing of natives or their undue exploitation, and made the law respected. He had amazing stamina, deep introspection and understanding and a weakness: He was envious to the end of his days of the results obtained in German New Guinea, sometimes reckoned superior; and he favored officers brought up in the tradition of the Australian portion, now called Papua.

The Second World War demonstrated the tremendous qualities of loyalty, courage and endurance the native of New Guinea possesses; it also demonstrated that, where they were not in close touch with the whites, they were not especially friendly toward us. The most "treacherous" natives proved to be the Benendieri, sometimes called Orokaiva, a tribe which, forty years before, had first come under the influence of a magistrate so belligerent that, in the Benendieri language, his name is now used as a symbol of aggression. To bully, beat up and bash a man is to "Monckton" him. Perhaps there is a connection between that and treachery, perhaps not.

Most of the white officers were gentlemen of exceptional courage and resource. In Papua they were known as Resident Magistrates, in New Guinea, on the north side, as District Officers. Today they are all District Officers, and in each district are served by an organization of assistant district officers, patrol officers and cadet patrol officers, together with a highly knowledgeable force of native police-men.

In the more settled districts which comprise the largest portion of the area these District Officers attend to the petty litigation of the natives, the care and maintenance of roads, airfields and harbor installations, and to such mundane tasks as the maintenance of postal services and savings bank facilities, the training of squads of the Royal Papuan Constabulary and a general process of "show-ing the flag" throughout their districts.

But in more remote areas the patrols go out through the country, crossing pathless mountains, or threading moss forests, or negoti-ating sago swamps of unimaginable difficulty to open up new coun-try and establish a contact with the people. This task, sometimes through country where every step has to be cut, is tricky and hazardous, and there is no guarantee that any contact made will be a peaceful one.

In older days, when gold miners, hunters of the birds of para-dise, and recruiters of labor frequently went on into country that the patrols had not penetrated, they sometimes left a legacy of hatred which the patrol officer had to counteract. I know from my own experience that there is no easy answer to a display of old bullet wounds made by angry and heavily armed natives with whom you cannot hold verbal communication. And sometimes the wrong reply was given.

So today there are areas of "uncontrolled" territory gazetted; and these areas are forbidden to missionaries, traders, miners, an-thropologists and the merely curious. Only the Government men, a district officer, accompanied perhaps by a medical man, a patrol officer needing the experience and a squad of police, are permitted in these territories. Frequently in them the Government will itself recruit labor; and this labor will get the best of treatment. The

Government motive here is to take a recruit to civilization, give him nominal work, and teach him a lingua franca before he returns to his village, so that thereafter there will be a means of communication with his people. The best of the recruits will be appointed a village constable and will wear portions of the uniform of the constabulary. Or he will be made a village headman, if this appointment does not conflict with his previous position among his people. Until a reliable means of communication has been established and the temper of the new people known, the only contacts will be made by the District Officers and members of their retinue. It is not only an excellent system; it is the only possible system. But it makes the task of assimilation a slow one.

The remainder of the white population consists today of traders, planters, recruiters of labor, Government servants in a bewildering variety, servants of the transport facilities, and a constant thin sprinkling of anthropologists forever investigating the sex life of the indigenes, who display almost as many variants in this capacity as do Europeans. Similar variants.

A few miles beyond the settlements the natives are still in the pristine carefree state. Except for those few who have been exposed for two or three generations to European culture, there is no great desire in them to adopt our ways. The change is imminent but has not yet arrived. White customs, white religious beliefs, white innovations have had no very welcome reception. And I think that perhaps this can be attributed to the extension of a natural law postulating that implicit in every living thing are the seeds of its own destruction.

Perhaps some such natural law exists with regard to logic. Perhaps the strong current of logic, kept in a single channel, diminishes in strength throughout its lifetime. For there is little doubt that logic raised man from the primitive to whatever height we now

*occupy and continues to raise him; yet primitive man is logical;
more logical indeed than are any of the rest of us.*

*Each action of his stems from a plain motive. Each reaction is
countered directly. His probable response to any contact or any
given circumstance can be estimated, understood and itself countered. In the simple essentiality of his logic are located the factors
which have given birth to the legend of his lack of intelligence. He
has no lack of intelligence, only a poverty of inherited, copybook
wisdom. He reasons from A to B, and from B to C.*

*On one of the postage stamps of New Guinea is pictured a strong
impassive native in the uniform of the police, one Sergeant Merire.
I met Merire in Sydney, where he was being introduced to the
wonders of civilization—electric trains, and trains that run beneath
trains, and tobacco factories that turn out cigarettes by the million,
and other marvels of engineering.*

*I spoke a little of pidgin English, a decadent and abominable
means of communication which, through tuition, is Merire's lingua
franca and his common usage, and I thus became his civilized contact in this place of wonders.*

*He was not at all impressed with what civilization had achieved
in concrete and tangible form; or perhaps it would be better to
say, in the realm of technics.*

*But there is no turning back. Merire and his people must
advance or be eliminated.*

*Here is the simple position of the districts bordering on the
Sepik River, reduced to understandable figures:*

*The infant mortality of the area has been assessed, to the horror
of the casual statistician, at six hundred per thousand. In the seven
hundred mile length of the Sepik a dozen good hard-working doc-
tors and a squad of assistants could reduce this figure to, perhaps,
one hundred per thousand; or even to the record figure (established
in the Pacific kingdom of Tonga) of under thirty per thousand.*

But, for many generations, the population of the Sepik has kept pace with the river's ability to carry them. All the people are river people. Every man, every woman, and every child needs a canoe; and for every canoe, as built by native methods, a fine erema tree must be sacrificed. The growth of erema trees handy to the river has kept pace with the need, and the need is great, for in the hot moist climate the life of a canoe is limited, sometimes, to a single year.

If the infant mortality rate is reduced so greatly, the population, after a generation, will double in something like ten years. In another fifty years it will be something like thirty-two times the present figure. The demand on erema trees will be excessive.

However, civilization is more than equal to this demand. By the erection of a plywood factory it can be arranged that a hundred small boats can be made from a single erema. Work in the factory will reduce the numbers of people who need to use the river. The sale of preservative paint will mean that every boat will last ten years instead of one. The gallop toward starvation will be arrested and more.

Civilization is on its way. The native cannot be left to die as he will. The practice of head-hunting must be stamped out; the casual leaving to die of one of every pair of twins must be stopped, the living child must not be buried with the dead mother, the selling of live heads—living people doomed for sacrifice—for small sums of currency or shells must be made illegal, disease must be fought, epidemics must be averted, living standards must be raised to eliminate nutritional deficiency diseases, populations must be transported to wherever the staple diet affords more protein than does the sago palm of the Sepik swamps. These measures are being taken wherever a sufficient contact has been made. Public opinion will not have it otherwise.

But public opinion in the forest is the opinion of Sergeant Merire.

I do not attempt to give the remedy. In the stories which follow I offer instead the problems; and some few of the compromises which currently pass as the solutions.

The Sword
of Laughter

"WATCH IT," said the District Officer. "I want no
incidents. For God's sake don't start a scrap
unless you have to, but get yourselves back safe.
These United Nations boys are a bit too eager to criticize. On the
other hand, we've got to do something about the river. If you can
make a firm contact with the Wagidi people we've got the game by
the throat. They're the ones that give us trouble every time. Bring
back a half-dozen Wagidi boys and we'll have a peaceful river. But
I'd like you to get some of the January River people as well, and
some of the Arodinis.

"The Arodinis shouldn't be hard, they've had contacts, years ago,
but of course the attitude may have changed. With all these people,
if you can't get any recruits, see if you can arrange to meet the
women. If you can make contact with the women you'll know the
men trust you. But if you do make contact with the women, then
watch your boys. You've got the hardest part ahead of you. I wish
I were coming with you. Double guards, by the way, in the Wagidi
country."

"We'll look after it," Bert Adams said. He was a thin man, very
thin and slight, with a hooked nose and bent shoulders. He spoke

softly, and he was worshipped by the New Guinea boys who formed his entourage. The third member of the group was a young patrol officer, Jeff Davidson. These three, the District Officer, the assistant district officer and the patrol officer were sitting on a rock by the riverbank, and from the trees about them, vines of the lawyer cane were stretched to moor a floating wharf or raft composed of the split trunks of the limbom palms laid over a little fleet of carved canoes.

A seagoing launch was moored with ropes to the same tree trunks so that the floating wharf acted as a fender to keep it off the bank. The current swirled and boiled beneath the canoes.

"No point in waiting," said Adams, standing up. "We'll be on our way."

The District Officer stood up too. "Good luck," he said. "I'd give anything to go with you, but I've been up as far as the Wagidi three times now, and the last two times we started a shooting war. I don't think we did too much damage, but they'd remember me and be resentful."

"A better chance this time," Adams said. "At least we're not in canoes."

They shook hands all round, and the two younger men boarded the launch. She was an ex-army work boat, about fifty-five feet, with an almost-clear deck protected from the sun by an awning running all the way aft from the wheelhouse. Already she seemed crowded with men.

There were eight police boys, all picked hands. Basiki, a boy from Buka in the Solomons, blue-black and muscled like an athlete, had been posted on the river during the war, and when the fighting started he elected, in the absence of instructions, to stay where he was and keep order. He did so, magnificently, protecting the people in his care from enemy contacts even though he was right behind the Japanese lines, and sending in occasional reports to let his masters know how things were going. Kambi, born and bred on the river, had also fought there during the war. Nearly all the police boys had a clear understanding of the purpose and importance of the expedition.

Skipper of the launch was a cheerful Aussie named Cliff Peeble, a man who was at home wherever he laid his head at nights. Under him he had a crew of about ten boys, Tami Islanders who knew the sea and were happy wherever there was water sufficient to carry them. In addition there were houseboys and a steward. And, wildly excited, his face one huge grin, there was a compact little boy of about eight years whom they called Tomkins.

His was an important function. In theory, he was a youngster accompanying his father—one of the houseboys. In practice, his presence on the launch gave authenticity in savage eyes to the proposition that the party's function was peaceful. A raiding party would not have bothered itself with children. It was impossible, with the concentration of men on the launch, to carry women, and indeed, women conventionally dressed might not have been regarded as female by the natives of the upper river. A child, playing happily on deck, sitting and watching the scenery float past him, even bawling his head off in a tantrum, was the next-best hostage to good faith.

Tomkins never indulged himself in tantrums. The scenery, though after a day it might have been counted monotonous, always provided something to look at—a native village, standing in the water; an eagle's nest as big as an army truck, crowning a tall fig tree; a crocodile, swimming ahead of the launch; big blue and bronze goura pigeons the size of turkeys, with dainty blue top-knotted crowns, preening themselves in the tall timber, prominent sometimes against the scarlet blaze of the D'Albertis creeper that cascaded down the green hillsides.

Toward evening the hornbills would fly screaming over the launch, and the flying foxes emerge from their cities behind the sugar cane to range the land and raid the native gardens in the bush; and for a few brief moments the sunset bathed the water in fantasy. The reflection in the east seemed always finer than the light surrounding the sun's bed. It soared all rose and carmine above the dark forest and every color was reflected in deep detail in the muddy water. They anchored at night always, and set a watch of Tami Islanders to ward off the heavy tree trunks that swirled down on the current and threatened their anchor chain.

It was an idyllic voyage, but at least in those early weeks, Adams, the A.D.O., showed his worries. The significance of their quest was far, far greater than that of other, more elaborate expeditions. The people of the upper river were isolated by much more than the physical difficulties of the country, which, in actuality, were rendered slight by the great navigable river itself. Even here, three hundred and fifty miles from its mouth, it was enormous: twenty-five feet deep and broad and fast-running.

But along its upper length each tribe was isolated, speaking its own language, hiding its habitations away from enemy eyes. Each tribe was constantly armed against its neighbors, whom they raided solely for the purpose of taking heads. They took no prisoners, and never learned each other's language. The upper river was classified as "uncontrolled."

Yet only trade could open up the river. Only trade could inspire the contacts which would discourage the inter-tribal wars; which could help to control the many and manifest diseases; which could make friends and future allies for the Administration. The Wagidi people, the most warlike and the most numerous, formed the key tribe. At least some of their members had, somehow, to be taught a language through which the recruiters and the traders could approach them. And the only way in which this could be done was by bringing some of the younger men to civilized areas and teaching them, word by word, in the way a baby is taught. Somehow they had to be given the desire to learn. The blackbirder of the early days, using force and guile, did not have the problem; but the blackbirder's victims, returning at last to the villages from which they had been stolen, paved the way for the agents of civilization.

Under the limitation of preserving the peace at all costs, it was not so easy to lure young men from their villages into an alien scene. And Adams, personally, had a further, private worry. He had no real faith in Jeff Davidson, his patrol officer, a young fellow fresh from the new-fangled School of Pacific Administration. Davidson had spent some time in settled areas, close under the watchful eye of a district officer, and Adams had a sneaking feeling that his excellence in clerical work might not augur that steadiness under fire which the coming situation might demand.

"The great thing is, take it easy, don't panic, and think quick," he said, outlining some of their difficulties after dinner one night.

"The great thing is rum," said Peeble, the skipper, reaching for the bottle.

As usual they had eaten their dinner on deck, on a collapsible bridge table at which they were served by the smiling, deft steward, a native named Arnold.

"You're looking a bit worried, Bert," Peeble continued conversationally. "It's only another patrol."

"I *am* worried," Adams admitted. "The Wagidi have been fought off so often it's getting to be a habit. The Japanese war was no good to them. They didn't see much of it; but none of the patrol parties that passed here bothered to dicker with them. Just fought them off. And I daresay the Japs did the same. We don't know how many parties they may have had a brush with. And the postwar record isn't so hot. Four small expeditions, and three of them drew fire from the Wagidi and all of them failed to make other contacts."

"Let's give them a miss and go straight up to the January River," Peeble suggested. "No one will ever know the difference."

"Not much," Adams grunted. "With a couple of thousand Wagidi waiting between here and there for anything that floats. No, we clean up. We bring back Wagidi men and make a contact with the women, or the show's a failure."

"Anything special about these women?" asked Peeble, raising one eyebrow.

"Well, no. But we won't see a woman on the river until such time as these people trust us. If they bring out their women before we leave, then we can go back friends. Or at least we can be fairly sure of finding them friendly."

"It's a pretty universal behavior-pattern," young Davidson said earnestly, speaking for the first time and airing the anthropology he had learned at the School of Administration.

"The only behavior-pattern the Wagidi have shown so far has a murder-motif," Adams said. "It makes vile art."

The broad pattern of travel on the river varied little. Always there was a bank falling victim to the erosion of the swift current; and because the processes of Nature seemed hastened in that vivid, exaggerated tropical land, the erosion was carried out before their eyes. In every hour, it seemed, some immense tree shuddered gently, and swayed a little on its roots, then crashed into the river to remain anchored a while by the tangle of creepers that fastened its upper branches to the standing trees.

The current itself was full of arboreal wreckage. Tree after tree hastened down, twisting and turning; and in each day millions of feet of wonderful timber trees, erema, cedar, kwila and taun, slipped by to rot on some midriver mudbank miles downstream. Between the trees came floating islands, tangled masses of the root- and plant-fiber of the wild sugar. They were large islands, sometimes half an acre and more in extent, and once or twice they were occupied by living inhabitants: crocodiles or snakes, or contemplative river birds. Everywhere the muddy water was flecked by the floating yellow flowers of the mogas tree, the wild hibiscus that loves to grow with its feet in the water.

On the bank opposite the retreating forest there was nearly always an immense field of arrowed seed heads twelve feet high, where the wild sugar was in process of reclaiming land from the river as fast as the river hewed it from the other bank.

For sixteen days the party traveled through this rhythm of construction and demolition, and then came to Sennowi, a village on the edge of uncontrolled territory; and therefore the last of which the houses were built on the riverbank and visible to all eyes. Here they stopped and waited for two old men, two lapuns, very old and very wise, who had been expecting them. The two were naked except for a flying-fox skin apiece that they wore instead of a loincloth. They wore shells in ears and noses, and bands of opossum fur about their heads. They had wrinkled faces and soft, kindly eyes.

"Hereafter the atmosphere thickens up," said Peeble, for the old men smelt to high heaven. "You've taken your last breath of fresh air till we get back," he told Davidson. Ignoring him, Davidson asked Adams, "Why are we taking them? They're not interpreters, are they? I thought there was no one who could speak Wagidi."

"Call them interpreters," Adams said. "They claim to talk Wagidi, but the D.O. says they can't get more than a word or two across. However, it lets the Wagidi see we are interested in the people of the river. They will recognize these two for Sennowi people, and it might fire them with an ambition to come along for the ride themselves. You can never tell. Got to play every card in the pack."

At midday on the nineteenth day they came to the bend of the river where the previous Wagidi contacts had been made. A tributary joined the main current here, and at the junction was a delta of islands, all crouching low in the water and all covered with the wild sugar. The confluence of the rivers was wide, a square mile or more of open water at the edges of which currents ran in all directions among the adjacent islands. The forest lay well back from the water. There was no sign of man.

The launch cruised slowly about the confluence. In four places the near horizon was broken by the tracery of the upper branches of breadfruit trees, sure sign of human habitation; but in none of these four instances could the launch approach the breadfruit groves because of the tangled mass of growing sugar. When they cruised too close the propeller fouled, and four times in the afternoon Cliff Peeble sent boys diving to clear the blades.

When night closed down the drums began, a rolling reverberation that leaped up at them from the water, and gave little clue as to the direction from which it came. Adams set a double guard of four police boys, and saw personally to the ammunition in their service rifles. Cliff Peeble supplemented this guard with two boat boys, who manned a searchlight on the roof of the wheelhouse. The drums continued without a break in the rhythm. There seemed to be thousands of drums, rolling in like thunder, and like thunder sounding, now near, now far away.

The searchlight circled the launch and picked up, among the roots of the sugar, the brilliance of red reflectors, in closely set pairs. There were dozens of these pairs of red lamps, all on a level at the surface of the water. None of them moved while the light was on them, but sometimes, when it had switched and then returned, the lamps were in a different place.

"Crocodiles," said Adams.

"I'm going to have a go at them," Peeble announced. He was fondling his own rifle, another service model.

"No you don't," Adams said. "The Wagidi know that sound too well. From now on, and while we're here, every shot fired from this launch must kill a man. No bluffing, no wounding, and no misunderstanding about shooting crocodiles. And, I hope to God, no shots fired at all."

Adams woke frequently that night from his sleep under the mosquito-net on deck, where he lay surrounded by the brown, uncovered bodies of the boys. Each time he woke the drums were unending and unaltered. In the morning they still throbbed, and Adams felt his head throb with them. But the guards reported nothing in the night, and the morning light disclosed nothing.

All that day they cruised slowly about the mudbanks. In the afternoon a canoe emerged from the reeds a long way off, with four men standing in it. They were visible only a minute; then the canoe vanished in the reeds again. The launch sped to the spot, but there was nothing. One of the lapun men from Sennowi grasped Adams by the arm and pointed. Adams saw a tiny movement in a tree standing back among the sugar. It could have been from a bird or an opossum. Because of the lapun Adams knew it was a man. The drums were beating unceasingly, and there was a droning of wooden trumpets.

After he had seen the man in the tree and verified that he was under observation, Adams went round the mudbanks at a little distance from the backwater they had used for anchorage. In the mud of each he thrust a bush knife, and draped over its handle a length of red cloth. At the foot of each of these little memorials he set out a mirror, a safety razor blade, a pair of fishhooks. He did this wherever the launch could safely approach a bank close enough for the police boys to jump ashore.

That night, because of the tension, they sat till midnight round the little table, drinking rum.

"We make a wonderful target," Peeble said, and poured himself another drink. They did, too. They made a brilliantly lit island in the sea of the night.

When he went to bed, Adams slept the night through, and awoke considerably refreshed in the morning. The guard reported mysterious splashings in the water, fairly close at hand, and attributed the noises to crocodiles. The gifts set out on the mudbanks were gone.

Adams waited a few hours, then set out patiently to replace the bush knives and the red cloth. The launch had just turned away from the second little depot when there was a shout from the police boys. Adams looked quickly, and saw a flash of red disappear among the wild sugar at the first spot. Immediately they turned back, and he tossed another knife onto the bank. Nothing happened there, but a hundred yards away a canoe prow nosed into the river. In the canoe an old, old man stood, grasping the rim of the wooden shell between the toes of his right foot, and wielding his paddle hesitantly, ready to turn and flee.

Adams ran to the case of bush knives, and held one out, grasping it by the point of the blade. The old man dipped the paddle, came a little nearer. Adams waved the knife and called for a length of cloth. Basiki ripped a yard and a half from the roll and handed it to him. Adams swiftly wrapped the blade in the cloth, and the old man paddled a little closer. He was shouting some unintelligible monosyllable. The two lapuns from Sennowi village jumped to the rail beside Adams and called. The old man hesitated again, then in a few swift strokes he came alongside and accepted the presents.

"Look!" called Peeble. There was a buzz of excitement from the men aboard. Out of the sugar, in every direction, canoes were emerging. There were dozens of them, each manned by from one to eight natives. They were shouting as they came, paddling furiously with a peculiar motion, swinging sharply from the waist as they dipped the paddles.

"No more presents," Adams called. "Trade only." He held a knife high as a native reached for it, and signaled for the man to give him his paddle in place of it. The man lifted up the paddle eagerly, and Adams handed down the knife. The native grinned his delight, and gathered up three other paddles from the bottom of the canoe to make another trade, quite unconcerned about the extra work he would have paddling home with the butt of his spear.

On board the launch, the boat boys broached a case of packets of fishhooks, and a case of mirrors. They set to work ripping the cloth into lap-lap lengths, and the trading began.

"You've got them feeding out of your hand," Davidson called.

"Take another look," Adams returned. "Except for the first man, every one's a warrior. The old man was just bait. Expendable. Look in the bottom of the canoes."

In every canoe a fire burned on a shard of pottery near the bow. Every inch of the remainder of each canoe was crammed with weapons—bow and arrows, fish spears with twenty points, blade-shaped canoe paddles that doubled as spears. In some were a few toys, spinning-tops and carvings. Some carried a little food, and some had garden implements—stone adzes, hafted in wickerwork. But nearly every canoe was crowded with an armament of lethal weapons which the launch crew were now buying rapidly.

"I think we made it," Peeble shouted happily, but at that moment there was a cry from up forward. One of the crew had found a native's arm investigating a porthole. Adams suddenly thought of his military position.

"Get them all around the portside," he called. It was hard to hear his voice above the din. "No trading on the starboard side, and no trading at all till all the canoes shift round. And Jeff, count the heads. I'll take a count myself."

By signs the wild men were instructed to go round the portside of the launch. Here they laid up the canoes side by side, and dropped their feathered and ornamented paddles at right angles across the narrow hulls, making a floating platform of surprising stability alongside the launch. The men were all excitedly bidding for trade now, making cutting motions with the edge of a hand against the crook of the other arm to indicate a bush knife, putting a finger inside a mouth to imitate a fishhook.

"Eight hundred, I make it. As near as dammit," Jeff Davidson said.

"Two hundred and twenty canoes," supplemented Adams. "They know what steel is, anyway. Let's try them with salt."

He had a bag of salt brought up, and distributed it in handfuls. The men tasted it; then threw it in the river or the fires.

"The first crowd I've ever seen that didn't value salt," Peeble commented.

They were ugly-looking customers. They were short, with skinny legs, but magnificent arms and chests. Three-quarters of them were suffering from the skin disease called grillae, an exaggerated tinea that gave them scales like fish. Many of them had elephantiasis. All were stark naked except that they wore daggers of bone in their arm bracelets and braided lockets about their necks, and talismans and decorations wherever they could hang them. One man wore a breastplate of pigs' tusks. Others wore cowrie shells, and Adams noticed that many of the elders, men about thirty to fifty, wore four of these in a curiously flowerlike pattern at the point of the nose. One man wore a breastplate of flashing blue wings of the kingfisher, and one had a long tail of bright green and white and black feathers, spaced out in blocks of color to form a simple design.

Some of the ten-foot paddles were decorated with red and yellow parrot feathers, some with the feathers of the white cockatoo and the black hornbill. Adams avoided buying the feathered paddles, because he had watched the canoemen clean their hands and their mouths and their noses on them. The smell of humanity in the raw —the rankest animal smell on earth—was all-pervasive, in spite of the acrid honesty of wood smoke that drifted over the scene from the fires in the canoes.

When there was a lull in the shouting, Adams became suddenly aware that the beating of the drums and the braying of the wooden trumpets had ceased.

Now the trading was in the hands of the crew, and Adams, with the help of the two lapun men from Sennowi, tried to talk with the leaders of the men in the canoes. "Tell them we want to see the village," he said again and again, and pointed repeatedly to the breadfruit trees behind the swamp that undoubtedly concealed a habitation of some sort. He called little Tomkins to him and stood with his hand on the boy's shoulder, trying to be oblivious to the fact that the boy, with a couple of fishhooks in his possession, was trading like an oldster.

Opposing Adams, the initiative seemed to be all in the hands of one of the men who stood in a canoe by himself; a huge fellow with a clean skin and a curiously Semitic appearance which was enhanced by the way he wore his hair, shaved back to the crown, and thence hanging in ringlets to the back of his neck. Peeble had already christened him Tracy, after another officer in the service to whom the chief bore no resemblance, other than in the slow speed of his reactions.

Chief Tracy at last appeared to accept the meaning of what he was being so insistently told. He shouted volubly, pointed to the breadfruit trees, then again far to the south, then traced the passage of the sun across the sky. Two or three of the others looked up at his shouts, and some of them began to echo his words.

A lapun reached out his skinny hand and touched Adams on the arm. His fellow lapun was bartering the shells from his ears for a necklace of dogs' teeth and had apparently lost interest. But the first one said, "Tomorrow. We see the village tomorrow."

Adams had already come to the same interpretation, and with it he had to be content. He was worried, now, as to whether he could disperse the wild natives before nightfall; but with the sun still above the horizon there came the vibrant bray of a wooden trumpet, resembling in its note the sound of a conch shell; and the canoes shot away from the launch as though their occupants obeyed a military signal. In seconds the river was empty again. There was no sign anywhere of the Wagidi.

Long before morning light, the sounds of men dickering with the watch brought Adams from under the blanket. He spoke sharply to the police boys, telling them to send the tribesmen away; but he found that was impossible. The trading went on with the greatest of enthusiasm. One of the canoemen pointed to a puckered scar on his chest and another on his arm that were undoubtedly bullet wounds.

Adams seized on the gesture immediately. He had one of the Tami Islanders lie down to imitate a dead man, and asked in mime, "How many?"

"What the hell are you doing?" asked Peeble.

"I want to know how many Wagidi have been shot. I want them to talk about it, to us. They are less inclined to do anything else about it if they talk," Adams told him.

The man with the healed wounds was making motions, but if they referred to men killed there were indeed a great many. Hastily, Adams offered him some trade.

Late in the morning, when the sun had come to a good height, Chief Tracy arrived and signaled for the launch to follow his canoe. He seemed to have some understanding of the draught of the launch and kept to reasonably open water. They followed him through winding channels and finally came to a place where a great pond opened out on the edge of forest.

In the water, four large houses stood on piles. At a distance of perhaps sixty feet from the nearest house, big floating tree trunks had been lashed one to another with lawyer vines in such a way that they formed a great log boom about the village. Within this boom, and leading from it to the doorway of the nearest house, a huge log was moored as though for a footway. Elsewhere in the pond were floating pigsties, strong miniature houses on solid rafts that could defy the crocodiles.

But there were no pigs in the sties, no people in the houses. There were no women, no children and no dogs.

Adams looked his disappointment.

The Semitic man he called Tracy was gesturing toward the houses, looking pleased. He brought his canoe to the side of the launch and signaled Adams to get in. Adams looked him straight in the eye and talked as though to him, but loudly for the benefit of the others on the launch.

He said, "Well, we've been sold a pup. This is a supplementary village and they cleared out the women before they showed it to us. It could be a trap. Tracy here wants me to go ashore and I'll have to show some trust in him and go. Jeff, come with me. While I go inside the huts stay outside where you can watch me and Cliff at the same time. Cliff, keep us both covered, and keep all the canoes between you and the huts. None at the rail or behind you. Jeff, if your Webley isn't loaded, go below and load it out of sight. That's about all, except for God's sake no shooting."

He climbed over the rail and sat himself squarely in the middle of the canoe. Tracy shouted, and set off for the boom with enthusiastic strokes. Jeff Davidson signaled over another canoe and got into it. Already dozens of men were crowding over the log boom, pulling their canoes into the pond, penetrating the huts.

Arrived at the boom, Tracy held his canoe off a little and harangued the people. He spoke at length, and in the meantime the canoe carrying Davidson came to the boom, was pulled over with the patrol officer still seated in it, and was taken to the doorway of the nearest hut.

Adams scented treachery, and his spirits fell with every word the man uttered. Yet, looking back, he realized he had followed, in his own actions, the only course open to him. Had he refused to look at the village on the ground that no women or children were there, he would have laid his motives open to suspicion. For these men, as the men of every other race, held that, of all women on earth, their own were the most desirable. He had followed the only course, but now the expedition to the empty houses looked very much like an attempt, and a successful one, to divide the forces on the launch.

No riverman would allow himself to be seated in a canoe. Sitting was for women and children and the very old; and not for warriors, who preferred to maintain a standing balance in these trickiest of all craft. In that moment, sitting in the canoe by the log boom, Adams understood the psychology behind the tradition. He felt overawed by the orator towering above him, for orator the man was. The chief's muscles tightened visibly as he clenched and knotted his words into a fabric of meaning. What was the design of the fabric? Adams wished he knew. If these were, as they seemed, the words of a tyrannous sovereignty, then, Adams felt, this was the end. He envisaged, quite clearly and calmly, another expedition sent out to recover his bones and ascertain his fate.

From a rapid calculation he could estimate that at least five hundred warriors, fully armed, had accompanied the launch to these empty houses, these deserted hunting lodges on the backwater. In addition there could be greater numbers concealed in the forest. Treachery was in the air, as it was, indeed, in the tradition of the Wagidi.

Adams felt, secretly and nervously, for the big service Webley in the pocket of his shorts. Its weight was reassuring when he hunched his right shoulder, yet he knew the revolver could do little for him. Its use would serve only to quicken still keener deceptions, practiced still more cleverly by the tribes people when next the white men essayed the navigation of the upper river.

At that moment all three white men were tensed, their perceptions honed keen by the long minutes of suspense, and all three of them thought according to their natures. Adams thought of those coming after him. In addition he consciously measured the distance to the launch, trying to estimate his ability to swim to it underwater if the need should arise; in his imagination counting the number of strokes, the number of brief appearances for air he must make, the way he must swim to the far side so that he could clamber aboard sheltered from the showers of arrows.

On the launch itself, Peeble felt the tension growing, conjured from the air by the incomprehensible Wagidi words. He was the practical man, the man who did things. He had brought the launch upriver, and by all the oaths he could muster he would take it down again. It was nothing to him that this or that great purpose should be defeated in the detail of achievement. It was his task to run the launch, to look after his own skin, and to stand by his friends.

So first he moved among the police boys, seeing that their rifles were in shape. But there was little need for that. They formed a picked team. He buckled on his own revolver in its holster, brought out the service rifle he used for crocodiles; and after a moment added the rifles belonging to Adams and Davidson to his arsenal.

Chief Tracy was still talking.

At the door of the hut Davidson's attention was divided. He was hemmed in by primeval man, and primeval man was taking himself seriously. In addition Davidson was suffering acute physical embarrassment. Probing fingers were investigating his skin, to see that it was not painted. They were feeling below his clothes, to ascertain that he was built in their own image and substance. They pulled at his hair, prodded his back. It took little imagination to arrive at the conclusion that those fingers were estimating the amount of meat he would provide for the victory feast.

So close was primeval man, Davidson could hardly move. He made the effort, as a kind of check on how quickly he could produce his useless revolver carried, like Adams', in a pocket of his shorts. He sought in the other pocket and produced, with some difficulty, cigarettes and matches, and lit a smoke. On an impulse he handed the lighted cigarette to the man next him. The man drew deeply on it, then passed it on. The faces about him were suffused with delight, as though a movie-director had commanded the emotion.

Among them were faces which, but for their strange coiffures, closely resembled many he remembered having seen on the streets of Western cities. It seemed to him that these were people he knew, for all that they smelt horribly of dead opossums and rancid humans. They were probably men with individual reputations for kindness, for cruelty, for greed, for thoughtfulness. Some of them, like the talking chief, possessed a capacity for oratory; some, probably, expounded a sound philosophy, and some had a sense of humor.

A sense of humor? Davidson brought himself back to the present with a jerk. This was a hell of a fine time to be thinking of a sense of humor. This was a moment of drama, such as he might never see again. If they ever got through this . . .

And at that moment, Chief Tracy threw his hands in the air, having arrived, apparently, at the end of his speech, and having, Davidson thought, probably decided the fate of the white strangers.

He looked about him for a tightening of hands upon weapons, but there was none. The men stood impassively, thronging about him, except for those still passing his cigarette butt from one to another. He lit another cigarette and a third, and started them on their travels.

The chief was climbing up on the log boom, extending a hand to Adams, shouting to the natives on the anchored log, obviously telling them to make a way. The white man took a step along the log. It rolled heavily in the water, and he lost his balance. In that instant, the chief, behind Adams, gripped him high on both fore-

arms and held them close against his back, making it impossible
for him, if he wanted, to draw the revolver from his pocket.

It could have been to save him from the water. It could have
been to hold him prisoner.

So in that same instant the police boys sighted along their rifles,
tensed and ready against this quickening emergency. On such a
tiny peg hostilities hang their beginnings.

The police would hold their fire till they were ordered. But Cliff
Peeble had also reached for his gun and was bringing it to his
shoulder. Adams saw it, and he saw also the irresistibility of the
impulse which would hold Peeble to his intent until he had pressed
the trigger. This was the end, Adams thought, and he threw himself sideways into the water just as he heard the sound of the shot.

He heard something else too. He heard the sound of loud and
raucous laughter.

With him went Chief Tracy, and thereby, all unknowing, saved
himself from Peeble's bullet. Underwater the chief still held Adams
tight, and he surfaced as quickly as he could. The water was only
neck-deep; but it was not until both their heads were clear that
the chief let him go. They stood in astonishment. All the natives
were in a pose of arrested movement. Only Davidson was laughing. He was laughing like a circus clown, bending himself double,
throwing his arms about, making all the noise he could.

Then from the launch came another cry. Basiki was balancing
on the rail with his back to the river, waving his arms wildly like
the wings of a crowing cock. He balanced only a second, and then
fell in, flat, spread-eagled on the water on his back, and sending
a splash up all over the boat. Then, at that sight, the tribesmen
clustered round the huts began to laugh, and Adams, laughing
himself, knew that the mounting tension was vanquished, felt it
disintegrate, as though a man, menaced by all the phantasmagoria
of a nightmare, were to open his eyes and find himself safe and

serene, comfortable in bed, composed in mind and body. He would never know what had been in the intent of his adversaries, or whether, in fact, they would have become adversaries unless under the compulsion of Peeble's bullets. He would never know how close death had passed him by. He knew only that he was safe.

He waded to the hut; and as Davidson extended a hand to help him up he said, "Thank God, you've got a sense of humor."

Davidson answered, "I never felt less like laughing in my life."

The inspection of the huts was anticlimax. There were huge baked clay pots made, like Roman wine jars, on a pointed base, so that they could not stand by themselves. There were tubular sleeping bags woven from grass so finely as to be mosquito-proof. There were flat clay fireplaces, and sago basins folded out of palm sheaths, and flails and a betel mortar; a big variety of household objects. Davidson stood guard at the doorway while Adams looked at these things, and later Adams stood guard for Davidson. He was still shaken by the moment on the log.

They stayed at their first moorings among the Wagidi two more days, but they made no further advance in their relationship.

Somewhere beyond the sugar, among the breadfruit trees, they knew there were villages with women and children; but these stayed hidden and the villages stayed secret. From the launch they could not even hear the crowing of cocks, the barking of dogs, the squealing of pigs.

So they left the Wagidi, and went on up to the junction where the January River joined the main stream. There were no people here. The villages that explorers had reported were gone. There was no sign of life. They investigated a line of breadfruit trees, and they could see that at one time there had been houses there, but that they had fallen down and decayed.

But fifty miles farther up they found the Arodinis. By an incredible piece of luck one of the lapun men from Sennowi could speak some words of their language; and after the first excitements of contact had subdued, he easily persuaded ten of the young men to ship aboard the launch.

Indeed, he persuaded more, but Adams culled the group severely. He turned down all the men who looked weak, all who had bad grillae or elephantiasis, all who had open sores of any magnitude. When he got his recruits aboard, the police boys ripped off their ornaments, shaved their hair, scrubbed them with stiff brushes and wrapped them about with clean lap-laps. The bush boys were delighted. They had no words to tell their pleasure, but they lined up again and again near the bucket and the scrubbing brushes.

"Well, we've got something to show," Davidson said.

"It doesn't solve the main problem, though," Adams commented. "The Wagidi still control the river, and we have neither their friendship nor their confidence."

"Won't we contact them on the way down?" Davidson asked.

"I suppose so. It doesn't seem much use."

On the deck aft, Basiki was holding school. He had lined up all the new natives and was teaching them pidgin English. He caught one by the hair. "Girass," he said. He poked a finger gently at his eye—"Heye." Tapped him on the nose—"Noose." Pushed a finger into his mouth—"Maus." Then like a choirmaster he set them all to repeating—"Girass, heye, noose, maus."

Two days later they discovered that the strange noises had meaning, and from then on their education progressed rapidly.

Anchored again off the Wagidi confluence, Adams waited for the tribesmen to appear. When the canoes began to emerge from the sugar he groaned.

"Look at them. No women. Always prepared for fight. It makes you wonder whether anyone ever will sail the river and find the villages on the riverbank, and the kids playing in full view. Whether they're ever going to feel it safe to live in the open."

The chief, Tracy, was in a canoe with a youngster of about eighteen years or so. The boy was looking open-mouthed at the ten new recruits, who stood in a block aft, visibly frightened, for these were their hereditary enemies and obviously very well known to them by sight. The boy spoke rapidly to the chief his father, and called out to the Arodinis, but they didn't answer. Father and son paddled rapidly to the side of the launch where, abandoning his paddle, the youngster sprang on deck.

Peeble shouted, and one of the police boys made a move toward the lad, but Adams held up his hand. The youngster addressed himself to the canoes, and made a speech as lengthy and apparently as eloquent as his father's had been before.

He spoke at length, then suddenly he walked to the rail, took the carved dagger from his arm bracelet and handed it to his father. He slipped a necklace of dogs' teeth from his neck, and handed that down. He stripped himself of every adornment until he stood naked on the deck.

"He's recruited himself," said Peeble.

He had done more than that. As soon as Adams realized the youth's intent he gave him presents—a bush knife and a mirror—and signified he should give them to his father. Then the police boys wrapped the lad in a lap-lap. Immediately there was a rush of youngsters from the other canoes. Adams selected ten of them, and signified that that was all.

And now the father of the boy, standing alone in his canoe, turned toward the waste of sugar cane and called, his voice high. There was an answering call, far and faint.

Adams said, "Well, let's get on our way before they change their minds."

The Tami Islanders went forward to the anchor, and the boy followed them, out of curiosity. When he saw what they were about he ran back to Adams, gesticulating. It was obvious he didn't want the launch to sail, and Adams indulged him, wondering.

"I'll give you twenty minutes. Then we sail," he said to the uncomprehending youth.

Just as the twenty minutes were up another canoe pushed out of the sugar cane with two seated figures. They were women, rather elderly and nearly naked. They pulled quite fearlessly up to the starboard side of the launch, which Adams had kept clear, and the youth went to the rail and talked to them.

One of them looked up at Adams, pointed to the boy, and then cupped her breast, telling him clearly that this was her baby.

"All right, Mother," he said. "I'll look after him."

She smiled as though she understood this perfectly, and presently she reached into the canoe and took a singed bird from the fire in the pot at the bow, and gave it to the boy. He accepted it absently and bit into it as he talked. Adams went below and found a bead bangle and a handful of loose beads and a couple of mirrors and a packet of razor blades, and handed them to the two old women. Then he gave a signal to Peeble and after a moment the boat moved into the stream.

In the evening, Adams went to the bow where Peeble was sitting, looking for a good anchorage.

"Well, the D.O. will be pleased. Successful trip," he said.

"It wasn't my fault," Peeble said gloomily. "We might have been still back there, the lot of us. I'm sorry about that shot. I really thought we were for it."

"Don't worry about it," Adams said. "It was the judgment of a moment. It's a damn' good job young Davidson had his wits about him. Laughing's about the last thing I'd have thought of. But it turned out for the best in the end. When you come to think of it, we all tackled it different ways—you shot, I got out from under, and Davidson laughed. And the laughing won."

From the afterdeck came the chorus of Basiki's school.

"Girass, heye, noose, maus," the boys chanted. "Han, foot, finga."

"Basiki's a good lad, too," said Adams.

"I thought he'd gone mad when he jumped off that rail," Peeble answered. "He had his wits about him." He paused awhile. "We'll make Sennowi tomorrow," he said. "Civilization four days later. There must be a five-knot current in this river."

Adams laughed. "Oh, civilization's a lot closer than it was," he said.

The river swept them along.

The Guardians
of Mobali

TOWARD noon, Bradding, at the head of the long file of men, reached the great limestone block that, with the abrupt definition of a Roman wall, marked the boundary between the semi-civilization of the lower country and the practically untouched savagery of the mountains. The block, as tall as a seven-story building and as perpendicular, stood where it had fallen centuries before, jammed between two high, unscalable cliffs that guarded the stream bed both above and below the obstacle. Down its face, a broad water-worn channel testified that floods created here a cataract of considerable magnitude; but the stream now emerged from below in a deep pool bordered by a litter of huge angular rocks at the base of the block.

The heavy forest continued along the stream borders right to the face of the sheer rock, where orchids clung, and were themselves entangled with creepers and the unluckier, stunted trees and bushes that had begun their lives in clefts and crannies instead of in the lush soil of the valley; but a small space was clear here, and had been enlarged recently by the hand of man; and those in the lead of the party, as they came to it, exhausted by the waist-deep scramble among the boulders and the swift tumbling waters of the stream, flopped where they could in attitudes of abandonment.

Behind them, the remainder of the long straggling file came like-wise to a halt. The carriers sought the clearer spaces along the bank, or more restricted perches on rocks and stranded tree trunks in the creek. They rested their loads and rolled foot-long cigarettes of twist tobacco in squares of newspaper for their relaxation.

The advance party had done its work well. Four slim trees had been felled against the limestone block and now, stripped of their branches, they lay with their tips nearly touching in the depression that floodwaters had carved at the top. Up the whole height of the trees, short spars had been lashed horizontally at intervals of perhaps two feet, so that there was an enormous ladder reaching to the top of the block. At its narrow apex the members of the advance guard, four lithe and active men in the uniforms of the New Guinea police, were scrambling like monkeys, lashing additional uprights to the top of the ladder where its strength was least.

They had done a workmanlike job. As it appeared now, the negotiation of the barrier offered no considerable difficulty, and Bradding, for the twentieth time since the expedition had set out, marveled at the foresight and expert generalship of the old cam-paigner, Major Canley. In a few short weeks under Canley, who was his District Officer, he had come dangerously close to a hero worship which was dampened only by Canley's uncompromising habit of keeping at a distance—even in circumstances such as these in which the two of them, reinforced by a dozen police boys and a small army of carriers, were the advance guard of a new way of life, of which the attractions might be far from apparent to the in-habitants of the mountains.

Canley now appeared in the clearing, having moved up from the rear of the column, examining the condition of the carriers as he came. He hesitated only briefly, and at once advanced on the ladder, working backward and forward on the horizontals of the lower levels, inspecting every lashing as he went. When his methodical progress took him to the top he spoke to the police boys working there, suggesting two places for strengthening, and pointing out a gap of rather more than the desired height. Only after that did he come back beside Bradding and sit down.

"Some of the boys are in bad shape, Ron," he said. "I think it might be wise to send a party back. These canoe people are pretty soft when it comes to marching."

"Will you send them back from here?" Bradding asked.

"No, we'll wait till we get on top," Canley decided. "I don't know what we'll find up there. From the air you can see nothing but a deep crevice. It widens out three or four miles above the block. It will probably be rough going in there. First thing is get all our gear on top of the block."

"Are you going to set up a guard?"

"You bet," said Canley. "Send them up first. I don't anticipate interference. But the Mobali people up above have the reputation of being tough customers. They're connections of the Baraps; the Baraps have known for the last week we are heading for Mobali country, and the chances are we're expected. If the Mobalis put up the same fight against the Government as the Baraps did, years ago, we might have some trouble on our hands."

"The Baraps look fairly quiet now," said Bradding, nodding toward a group of Barap carriers.

"Yes, they've changed a lot," Canley agreed. "But they're still the toughest babies in the controlled territory. They used to be a really bad bunch. They got cleaned up before my time, though. I've never had any trouble with them, to speak of."

In spite of the preparations, the transit of the limestone block was long and arduous. The men halved loads, and struggled up the laddered face two or three at a time, returning to help the others. At four in the afternoon a carrier, a thin and gangling man with the crocodile scales of grillae etched deeply into his skin, fell from a crossbar to the jagged rocks and broke a leg. Bradding set it with speedy efficiency, and had the police boys who were supervising the operation on the rock construct a litter. Canley came down from the top where he had been seeing to the establishment of a camp.

"That settles it," he said. "A party turns back tomorrow. I'll arrange a redistribution of the loads, and we'll see who we can take."

The sudden nightfall of the tropics found the whole party, except for the injured man and a small guard, encamped at the top of the limestone block. Here was a narrow and fearful chasm, a vast cleft from which, to one side, they looked out over forested country. But looking forward they saw only the vast mouth of this echoing rift, floored with naked rock, irregular and water worn. Paradoxically, it had been difficult to find shelter here, but nearly all of them were eventually disposed in a series of shallow caves, little more than depressions high up under the overhanging cliffs and safe from any freshet in the stream which, two hundred yards above the edge of the block, disappeared among its boulders as magically as it reappeared below.

In a corner of the gorge Bradding and Canley found a small shelter big enough for the two of them; and here they were able to camp without a tent. They also had a degree of privacy; though this, in general, they neither sought nor much appreciated. Upstream from them were the three guards on duty. In all other directions the overhanging cliffs lent complete protection to the little army.

Bradding, however, was restless. The gorge, lit fitfully by spurts of flame from one or other of the little fires, was an awesome place, its atmosphere heavy and brooding. Only overhead, in a river of skydarkness, they could see a few of the stars, and among them a planet hung like a heavy lamp. There was an utter stillness in the gorge, a dead suspense of mobility which was emphasized rather than broken by the occasional muted sounds and movements among the police boys and carriers. Twice, after they had finished their meal, Bradding got up and walked about the camp, watching the carriers bedding down, inspecting the guard, taking a look over the edge of the block to the subsidiary camp at its foot.

Within ninety minutes he got up for the third time, and Canley spoke to him sharply.

"Sit down," he said. "Sit quiet." There was a bark in his voice that Bradding resented, but he sat down and waited, without comment.

"You've been prowling about like a cat in an earthquake," Canley complained. "If I thought that was typical of you I'd have left you behind. You'll get the men nervous, and God knows this place is enough to make them nervous without you helping to set them off."

"I'm sorry," Bradding said. "I wasn't thinking."

"Not true," said Canley. Bradding looked at him inquiringly. Canley's expression was earnest in the glow of the embers of their small fire. The night was cold, not tropical night at all.

Canley said, "I'd better have this one out. It could get worse—in fact, it's been getting worse. You don't know how much these fellows—" he gestured in the direction of the posted guard—"look to you. And how quickly they can sum you up. If *I* think you are acting as though you are frightened, they will too. And you *are* acting as though you're frightened. Are you frightened?"

Bradding didn't answer for a moment. He knew his man, and he judged that Canley's motive was a friendly one. To cover the delay he pulled out his cigarettes, noted that Canley was already smoking, and lit one for himself. With the match still alight he said, carefully, "I don't think I am frightened. I'm a bit strung up, that's all."

"Can you tell me why?" asked Canley.

"What a fantastic question," Bradding thought, "what a fantastic thing to be asked in this, of all fantastic places."

Aloud he said, "I suppose I could. It's a long story. I'm not actually afraid. Or at least I don't think I'm afraid of the Mobali."

"No. You're afraid of being afraid, I suppose," Canley said very quietly and sincerely. "That's inexperience, that's all. Comes to most people, sooner or later."

"I've wondered," Bradding said. He waited a little while, but the older man said nothing, and the desire to talk rose in him.

"It goes right back to the war. I had a damned unlucky war, in a way," he said. "Never saw it really, so only the fringes of it touched me. I joined the Air Force, a bomb-aimer. Got as far as the squadron in England, in February, 1945, and it looked like we were in it. My skipper was a great bloke, a Canadian; one of those characters they make legends about: good family, good sport, good company. And he was really spectacular. It wasn't good enough for him to be anything but the best. He was clever, too, but a bit of a show-off. He'd been in trouble for all the usual things: shooting up the field, looping practically off the ground, low flying—but those were the only black marks against him. High-spiritedness. The girls thought he was wonderful. Most of the fellows did too—I know I did.

"Well, here we were, on the squadron, and on top of the world. He was about the most popular new arrival there. And the night he was to make his first operational flight over Germany, as second dickey with an experienced crew, we were all there to cheer him on. But he wasn't. He'd left the airfield and gone uptown, walked up to a policeman and hit him on the jaw. So of course they shot him out of the service L.M.F.—Lack of Moral Fiber—and they split his crew and sent them back to operational training units. And by the time I picked up a new skipper, and went through the training all over again, and got back to a squadron, the European war was over."

"So you never knew about yourself?" Canley asked, quite shrewdly.

"That's right. Up to that time I hadn't worried, you know. I suppose I was a bit scared of the usual things—being shot down, being wounded—being burnt was the worst—but I didn't worry. But this skipper. Well, I don't know. He had everything, you see. And he had risked his skin a hundred times before he got to the squadron. Just the same, when it came to the final test he was keyed up for, he went out and socked a policeman. So after that—well, it's what you said. I'm frightened to death of showing yellow, I suppose. But until now I've never been up against it."

"I doubt that you're up against it now," Canley reasoned. "These patrols—even into uncontrolled territory—are seldom anything but routine. Nothing to worry about."

"There could be," Bradding disagreed. "Twelve rifles and you and I—how many people in the valley?"

"Not more than six thousand, I'd say," Canley said equably. "You're right, of course. We might be up against it. We never know. But the greatest weapon you have is self-control. Learn to use it. About being afraid—I can't help you. It's possible that you'll show yellow, though I wouldn't think so. The chances are you'll be all right. The chances are, you know, you'll be too busy when the time comes. Why I spoke to you is this: your responsibility begins long before that. The boys can sense that you have a fear; they won't bother to analyze what the fear is. They will not be sympathetic to any fear of fighting or of death. The main thing is to keep yourself under control."

"Well, thanks, Jim," Bradding said. "I didn't know I was giving anything away."

"You were," said Canley. "That's why I spoke to you."

It took them all morning and half the afternoon to negotiate the four miles between the overhanging cliffs to the point where the stream entered the gorge from a country of low hills. It rained heavily throughout the transit, and the carriers were working under strain, more because of the gloom and half-darkness of the gorge, the fear of a freshet in the river, and a movement in the tons of limestone poised over their heads, than because of the greasy, troubled track over the boulders. Yet several times police boys had to construct stages over massive falls of rock that blocked the party's way, and again they often had to travel through the rushing stream with the heavy packs. With the limestone gorge behind them they came out on cleared ground where native gardens had been maintained at an earlier date; and here, because of the strain on the carriers, Canley ordered a camp for the night.

As the carriers came in, set down their loads and began to erect their little palm-leaf shelters against the tropical rains which would, inevitably, continue to drench the late afternoon, it became obvious that the party would have to pause awhile and lick its wounds; and Canley decided to make a staging camp of their position. Seven of the eighty carriers had shoulders rubbed raw with the carrying poles and could go little farther without a rest. One of the armed constables was carrying in place of a man whose foot was badly spiked; and yet another constable, Ebidi, had his left hand mangled and his wrist swollen and sprained as a result of a fall among the rocks. So on the following day they waited while Canley supervised the construction of a safe cache for rice and tinned stores, dressed his men's wounds, and rested.

Early in the morning the eight Barap carriers and interpreters who, being fresh, were not among the casualties, came to Bradding with the proposition that they should go ahead of the main party and make contact with the Mobali in their village. They spoke through the police interpreter, Samsamiap.

"Sir," said he, "these people wish to go ahead to the village of the Mobali which, they say, is only an hour on the trail from here. They say that if they go first to tell the Mobali people that the Government is on its way on a visit of friendliness, then we will be welcomed when we appear."

"Tomorrow we will all go together," Bradding said. "There is no need for some to go and then the rest of us."

"Sir, they say they have many friends among the Mobali. Every year they meet them to trade with them. They say the Mobali, not knowing the Government, will otherwise lay an ambush for all the party, and there will be fighting. But if they go first they can smooth the way."

"What's this?" asked Canley, walking up from where a working party was erecting two huts sturdier than the shelters they had used overnight; and Bradding explained.

"It might not be a bad idea at that," Canley said. "Ask them, Samsamiap, whether they are very sure they will meet the Mobali in friendliness."

There was a short talk in the epiglottal Barap tongue.

"They are very sure," Samsamiap said. "They have been to the village before, and they are certain of their welcome."

"Ask them, though, whether they will still be certain of their welcome when it is known they have guided the Government," Canley insisted, and again the reply was in the affirmative.

"Then they can go," he decided. "But not all of them. We may need interpreters in the camp. We may be visited by the Mobali. Four may go, and four stay. And those who go will be back in camp here before the rains begin in the afternoon. I will be happy if they bring back visitors from the Mobali."

But in the afternoon there was no sign of the Barap party. At four-thirty on schedule, the rains began, and before the night came down at six the rains stopped, and the air cleared, and still there was no sign of the Baraps. Canley posted double guards about the camp and settled down for the night. But he was silent and morose, and Bradding could feel some tension. Long before morning light the police ate their rations of rice and bully beef, and with the first break of dawn both Bradding and Canley, supported by six of the armed constables, were on the trail.

They took with them two of the remaining Baraps and left two in camp, where the sergeant and the remaining five police, including the injured man, Ebidi, were left in wakeful charge.

The Barap estimate of an hour's walk proved inadequate, and that was a good sign bearing on the probable condition of the wild emissaries. It was perhaps an estimate conceived by Samsamiap, Bradding thought, in translation of some more elastic standard. At the end of two hours' walking, Samsamiap, who had been exchanging isolated sentences with the two Baraps, tugged on Canley's shirt sleeve.

"Sir," he said, "the Mobali village is close by." He pointed to a junction of trails just ahead of them, where the path they were following was joined by a broader, more recently used way. "Along this path the Mobali women go for water," he said. *79941*

The trail led between thick bamboo clumps, and now it turned and twisted, almost doubling on its tracks every ten or twelve yards. At the fourth doubling back of the path one of their Barap carriers sat, his back against a bamboo clump, his hands folded in his lap, his legs disposed neatly before him. He sat quietly, because he had no head. Instead, a black and ugly stump topped his shoulders, and black and glistening gouts and runnels of his blood had added their contributions to the elaborate ornamentation of his body. Canley looked at Bradding, and Bradding was white.

Canley said, "Bad show, eh?"

"It looks a bit dicey," Bradding agreed, and with a jerky convulsive movement shouldered his way into the lead and walked on, stepping high over the outstretched legs of the headless man.

Round the next clump of bamboos, on the next corner of the trail, sat the oldest of the four messengers. He, too, had his hands in his lap, his feet placed straight in front of him, his back against a clump of bamboos; and he, too, was without a head. Black blood glistened on his body, but there were no splashes of blood on the bamboos, none on the ground about him. The track curved round the bamboo clump and seemed to double back.

"Fix bayonets," Canley said, quite calmly, and he loosened the revolver in his holster. In the next two bends of the track they found what they expected to find: the other two Baraps, without their heads, with their backs against the bamboos and their hands disposed quietly in their laps. The third man had a deep grooved scar running down the sole of his foot. None of the others had a mark on him. Their bodies were perfect and undamaged from the shoulders down. There had been no struggle, no fight. Beyond the fourth man the track ran through an opening in a heavy palisade into a large village.

Bradding hesitated only momentarily at the palisade. Then he walked through into the center of the village and looked about him.

There had been fires lit in two of the huts on this morning, and blue smoke still drifted into the fresh and sunny air. A yellow dog ran suddenly from the back of one of the smaller buildings; a little group of hens pecked busily by the palisade. The huts were strong and of good workmanship, and the ground where they stood was clean, without litter. There were no people anywhere. There was no man anywhere, except for the four silent guardians of the entrance.

"It gives you the creeps," said Canley, pushing up alongside Bradding. The younger man said nothing, but walked forward and up the steps of the largest building, one of those from which a thin line of smoke drifted upward. There was an outer platform reached by a wide permanent ladder, and from the platform a small door opened into the building itself. Bradding squatted on the platform near the door, squinting this way and that to see whether or not the inadequate opening, which he could negotiate only by crouching low, was guarded inside by concealed warriors.

He was deathly afraid and he felt his fear must be obvious. But all his companions saw was a man squatting, a loaded revolver in his hand, looking this way and that through a doorway. Canley and a police boy named Ebargo were following Bradding up the steps, but they had not reached the platform when he dived quickly through the door. They followed immediately, to find him standing alone, his back against the wall which contained the door, in a great shadowed room. There were the coals of a fire still hot, and the air was filled with the appetizing scent of meat cooking. Bradding sniffed it appreciatively.

"That's not pork," he said. "It smells like beef. What is it? Is it wallaby or something?"

Ebargo stepped forward to the fire and took a sliver of meat from the embers. He brought it back and held it out wordlessly, and Bradding inspected it. Then Ebargo turned the piece over in his hand, and Bradding could see the stubble poking through the skin. It was from the cheek of a man's face.

Bradding turned quickly and dived back through the door into the open air. His stomach heaved convulsively. But he was aware that the constables were watching him, and he stopped himself from being sick.

They searched the village, but they found nothing and nobody. Nothing that could not have been duplicated in a hundred other villages. Though they could be reasonably sure that, from some vantage point, men watched them, there was little they could do, and they returned to the staging camp in the deserted garden.

For the rest of the day Canley and Bradding were busy. They inspected the whole line of carriers closely, and put on one side all those who looked as though they were failing after the struggle, which had been long; for they were now nearly a month from their base. To these they added certain disruptive spirits, men who were disgruntled with the job. Then they selected some of the older men to complete a big culling of thirty carriers who would, in the morning, take the trail back to their homes. The camp in the garden was strengthened; and Bradding bathed and poulticed Ebidi's injured hand and sprained wrist. The police boys worked quietly on their weapons, polishing the bright bayonets even brighter, and singing sad little songs with an abandoned gaiety.

Lying at night in the tent they shared, Canley and Bradding talked.

"This has forced our hands. We stay here now until we get the murderers." Canley's acceptance of a task that seemed formidable was remote and matter of fact.

"Why do you think it happened? *How* do you think it happened?" Bradding asked.

"God knows. Probably the Mobali just don't like the idea of Government," Canley said. "And how? They were probably sitting all in a ring, passing the time of day and smoking a pipe among them. Or having a meal. And all four got clouted on the head at once, to make a warning for us to stay away. Must have been something like that. There was no struggle, anyway."

The carriers sitting round the fires were afraid. Especially were the four remaining Barap men afraid. They sat silently and ate their rice and meat.

"Anyway, it showed you something," Canley said. "You took it all right. I didn't see any signs of you showing yellow."

"I've seen dead men, often enough," Bradding demurred. "I still haven't come face to face with anything in the nature of a real test. Not really. You see, there was no one there, in the village."

"I tell you there is only one enemy you have to beat, and that is yourself," Canley said. "The real enemy is never there. When you are ready for him you find an empty village."

"I'll believe that when I come to an enemy, face to face. Are we going to chase these blokes up tomorrow?"

"First I think we'll contact the other villages," Canley said, following the switch readily. "Maybe that will heap up trouble for us. Maybe not. But it would help to have someone on our side, if that's possible."

In the morning, when they followed the path from the garden, they branched off at the first junction of tracks, and after awhile they found themselves penetrating deeply wooded country.

Their original eighty carriers had now been reduced to thirty-four. The file was closer now, more compact, and the sergeant who brought up the rear had little trouble in keeping the laggards moving. They had proceeded perhaps seven miles through the forest when, from the head of the column, Bradding saw the faces in the undergrowth, three faces, briefly glimpsed.

He waited, while the party mounted up behind him.

"Kami, kami, kamio," cried the police boys, in greeting. They faced the wall of the forest where Bradding had seen the faces, and presently the men hidden there began to make themselves apparent. To the first who disclosed himself, Canley made a present of a wicked-looking bush knife. Presently they were faced by fifteen silent savages, each dressed in a kind of fiber harness that covered the shoulders and was joined to a belt at the waist; and each decorated otherwise with dogs' tooth necklaces and spoils of the hunt.

Only one of the fifteen men answered the questions which Canley now put to them. There was a long process of interpretation between Canley, Samsamiap, the eldest Barap villager and the new arrival; long cadences of words in a symphony in four languages, set about a fugue of misunderstanding and explanation; but through it all the others stood impassively, sullenly, perhaps, with their arms folded, and a stone ax in each right hand reared up against each left shoulder. Round the neck of a man in the rear was a necklace of what looked like black and withered mushrooms. Bradding looked at it for some time before he realized that it was composed of human ears, strung disc-wise.

"These are the men of the village of Sigibali," said Samsamiap. "They live in the mountains a little way off."

"Will they lead us to their village?" asked Canley. "Tell them we are the Government. We would like to look at their village, to walk about it, and to speak in friendship with their chief. We would like to make friends with them."

Rather to his surprise, the spokesman consented immediately, without consulting the others, and without taking time for consideration. But on the words the fourteen others turned, and vanished silently into the forest. The spokesman didn't seem to notice their disappearance. He led the way along the track they had been following, talking bright to all and sundry, not a bit concerned by the fact that only the Barap people understood his words.

The order of march was now: the Sigibali, then Bradding, then a Barap interpreter, and after him two police boys and Canley. The track was fairly open, and sometimes two or, in places, three of them walked abreast; and the footing presented no great difficulty. In general, however, the file of men walked singly. Though the way was easy, the weather fair and the burdens not onerous, there was no singing from the carriers, no shouting and chaffing, only a few muttered remarks from a man to his neighbor.

Soon they emerged from the thick forest and began to traverse the side of a steep hill, over country so covered with roots and creepers that it was more than ever a necessity to keep to the path. At the outermost extremity of the spur the track turned abruptly to the right and went uphill, following the ridge.

From the turn Bradding could see, well above him and in plain view, the heavy stockade of a fortified village. Behind the stockade, fully-armed men stood and waited in silent expectancy. At the same time, Bradding was acutely aware that the Sigibali guide was no longer in front of him, but was paying one of his bright, chattering visits to the rear of the line. The police boys were keen and thrusting behind him, almost pushing him in their eagerness. They were always spoiling for a fight, he thought. This looked like one.

It smelled, indeed, like treachery. The whole circumstance of finding the guide, of losing his companions, of following him into a place of his own choosing looked like treachery. So now, at the head of the line, pushed up the hill inexorably, it seemed, by the weight of opinion behind him, Bradding counted the men behind the stockade, making quick estimates of the little groups. He found them to number more than a hundred.

It was a long struggle up the ridge. Under the blazing sun of noon it would have been a struggle under the most peaceful of circumstances; and this was increased by the vulnerability of the climbers to the silent figures guarding the village. Behind the police boys the carriers fell silent and hung back; and once, near-panic developed among them when one of the leaders dropped his load and ran toward the rear, crying that a big fight was coming, that they would all be killed. A constable tripped the flying figure with a shrewd thrust of his great bare foot; and when the man had picked himself up, led him firmly by the wrist to the point where he had dropped his end of a carrying pole.

A little group filed silently through the open gateway of the stockade. They were directly above Bradding; had any of them dislodged a pebble it must have struck him, and he was absolutely and entirely at their mercy, the obvious and only possible first victim of the aggression that seemed imminent. For he could not even gather the police about him, but must toil upward, by himself, along the knife-edge of the ridge; his heart straining, but his mind unwilling, under the scrutiny of the savages, to rest it. To halt, to turn back, was to invite the attack. He kept going.

Three men stood in the center of the group of defenders. They were dour and evil-looking, warriors to the essence, formidable to the eye. Their noses were pierced with heavy bone, their hair was knotted and built up on their heads, their hands were ready with their weapons. They were poised like hawks before the stoop.

Bradding forced himself to an unwavering advance. There was no respite from the steep slope and he was breathing heavily. He stopped at last, three yards from the nearest man, his hands empty, his eyes fixed to the faces above him, his brain conscious of his inadequacy.

But at that moment the Sigibali guide came up, skipping over the obstructions at the side of the track, chattering like a magpie, threading his way along the line. Immediately the three savage faces lightened. The men greeted the guide and he spoke to them at length. In a little while they made a way, and motioned Bradding, with the file of men, into the village.

The events of the rest of the day were pure anticlimax. They gave presents to the chief, presents which he solemnly passed round the village for each man's inspection. Through the interpreters they spoke of the Mobali people; but here they drew a blank. The Sigibali pretended to ignorance of their neighbors, their habits and their whereabouts. Nor was Canley successful in buying village foods from the Sigibali. There were extensive gardens close by in the hills, but such fruits and vegetables as they saw were not of good quality, and for this Canley blamed the lack of fertility in the high mountain soil. Moreover the men did not respond to requests for such produce as they had, and Canley did not press them, guessing that the carriage of vegetables was women's work, that the men would not demean themselves with it, and that they would be unwilling to trust their women within sight of such a large party of strangers.

The whole company camped that night within the stockade, but neither women nor children came back to the village while they were there. Not wishing to become an embarrassment to acquaintances who might someday become friends, Canley ordered an early morning start, and they retraced their steps to the trail which led to

Mobali, having first given the chief and several of the elders a taste for rice and bully beef which might, Canley hoped, eventually prove as strong an argument as any other for co-operation with the Government.

The next night they camped in the Mobali village. Still deserted, it was apparently as they had left it, except that one of the policemen discovered footprints about the graves in which they had buried the four headless men of Barap; and in one, a lance had been thrust deep into the disturbed soil. The bones would be recovered at an early date, Canley thought, to make spear-tips and arrowheads for the Mobali. He said as much to Bradding, who nodded absently.

"Where do we go from here?" he asked. His lack of concern was supported by the knowledge that in their own village the Barap victims would have supplied the community similar artifacts on their death. It was a custom of the country, and one not worth making an issue over.

"They won't be far away," Canley said. "We camp here, for a start. And take out patrols to find them. I don't know what else we can do. But they won't travel out of their own territory, and this is too big a village for them all to hide completely away. Not the lot of them. They'll have a big hideout somewhere, big enough for us to find."

In the mornings Bradding, and in the afternoons Canley, each took five police boys and combed the trails, returning to trace on a rough map the route each had followed. In this arrangement Canley was taking the worst of it, doing his stint through the heavy rains that fell each evening, almost by the clock; and Bradding was keenly aware of it. Several times he offered to relieve the older man but was refused.

By the third day they had traversed, for a reasonable distance, each of the main trails and the more evident tributary paths that began in the area adjacent to Mobali. But they had not uncovered any trace of the villagers.

"It gets a bit eerie at times, when the bush closes over the road," Canley commented when he rejoined Bradding on the third night.

"You're telling me," said Bradding.

"You're making a good fist of it," Canley said. "You're doing all right."

"I still get butterflies in the stomach though," Bradding admitted. "I still haven't seen the enemy."

"What about Sigibali? Going up the hill? That was a bit touchy, if you ask me," Canley challenged.

"Yes, but you see, there wasn't any enemy," Bradding argued. "I only thought there was. I was imagining things again."

Canley grunted and changed the subject.

Next morning Bradding was only half a mile from the village on a track they had used several times when the sergeant who accompanied him stopped. There was a drift of leafy creepers hanging from the trees alongside the track in its widest place, and he swept them aside like a curtain. Behind the leaves, a thin and almost unobservable path led off at right angles. The camouflage was beautifully placed, in a spot where the eye naturally followed on to a turning of the main trail, and there was little wonder they had overlooked it.

The sergeant led off, and Bradding followed him, but after a few steps, realizing that he himself could distinguish the new path with ease, Bradding took the lead. The air was still chilly with the mountain dawn, the morning fog hung about them, not yet dissipated by the morning sun. They had breakfasted, as usual, in the dark.

The trail led straight into the lower valleys, winding about wooded spurs. They followed it nearly three miles, and suddenly it ran into a network of other trails, broadly defined. Away off to the right a human voice sounded in a weird falsetto that approximated the yodel of Switzerland.

"Run, master," called the sergeant. "Run quickly. We will find them."

His eyes were bright, his voice eager.

Bradding obediently broke into a run, rounded the corner of the track, and immediately came upon a collection of four large bush houses, built low to the ground. They were surrounded with a confusion of figures disappearing among the trees. But already, in front of the largest house, there was a nucleus of men standing armed, a nucleus that was growing rapidly. Here, at last, were the Mobali. Here, at last, was Bradding face to face with his enemy.

He burst into the clearing and stopped. And immediately the Mobali, shouting and posturing, advanced on him. They were armed with bone-tipped spears and stone axes, though here and there he caught the pattern of an old steel trade axe, or the long blade of a bush knife. They clustered about a leader, a big man, well-proportioned and heavy, a man with a lined and cruel face. In the glimpse he had, Bradding read the utmost determination on that face. He saw the whole picture of the man, so that in later years he would be able to reproduce it with accuracy, the light cane shield, black and shining, carried under the left armpit; the short bone-tipped spear, the shoulder harness, and the long ladder of pig tusks hanging like a breastplate from his neck. In the after-picture there would be an incongruous object, a tame cassowary stalking behind the man, taking no notice of the confusion, its attention centered on something on the ground.

"Above their heads," Bradding yelled. "Ready. Fire."

The short and ragged volley sounded like artillery in the silence of the bush and it worked a near-miracle, for the charging crowd stopped short and turned tail, and ran for the shelter of the trees. Only the leader came on and threw his spear, and switched his stone club from his left hand to his right. In the same instant Bradding dived for the man.

The spear ripped across his left arm, just below the short sleeve of his shirt. But simultaneously, or so it seemed, Bradding took the man in the groin with his knee, and smashed his revolver into his temple.

Afterward he thought that the man's aim must have been deflected by the shock of the volley and his own unexpected attack; for to the untaught eye, Bradding seemed a man unarmed.

The savage fell with Bradding clinging to him, and while he was falling an arrow came from the shelter of the trees, passed between Bradding's legs, and sank deeply into his opponent's thigh.

The savage hit the ground and lay still, and the sergeant appeared at Bradding's elbow.

"Sir, you are hit," he said. "I'll look after this fellow. You get in the shelter of the house." There were arrows coming from the bush, not flights of arrows, just occasional shafts. Most of them were flying wild but they were concentrated in Bradding's vicinity.

Bradding looked about him. Already two natives were handcuffed to each other with a tree between them, and Bradding grinned. He hadn't seen that simplification of custody before. Except for the sergeant, not a policeman was in sight. Two shots sounded separately in opposite directions from the clearing, and the sergeant lifted his head and called authoritatively. In a minute the other police boys came back into the clearing, bringing two more prisoners, one with a bayonet wound in the leg.

Suddenly aware, as one who comes out of darkness, Bradding felt the warm stickiness of alien blood on his leg, and looked to his capture—he was referring to him mentally as the chief, which apparently he was. The arrow still stuck in his thigh, below the groin, and the blood welled rhythmically up the shaft and spread out over the skin. The head of the arrow had found an artery.

Bradding dropped to his knees and examined the shaft before he withdrew it; but it was a hunting arrow, with a single broad blade of razor-sharp bamboo, and its removal presented no problem. He drew it out. As at a signal the shower of arrows from the forest began again, the shafts digging into the ground at an angle which showed that their flights originated from some vantage point in the trees that towered around. Bradding, his hands laved with the great arterial gushes of blood from the chief's wounded thigh, took no notice. He had stripped off his belt and was applying a tourniquet at the groin. The sergeant shouted orders to the police—who indeed were already headed for the edge of the clearing in the direction from which the arrows came—and then began a slow, queer dance behind Bradding.

"What the hell are you doing, sergeant?" Bradding snarled. He spared a moment from his ministrations and looked up. The sergeant had taken possession of the chief's cane body-shield and was skipping about with it, trying to protect his master from the flying arrows. Bradding considered him seriously for a moment, and then returned to his work. And the arrows ceased.

Three shots sounded from the forest. Bradding had finished his task when the police returned, with four more prisoners. They had found them treed in a huge and spreading fig, and persuaded them to the ground with the rifles. Three were undamaged. The fourth, the object-lesson, had a flesh wound in his calf.

"Good shooting," said Bradding. "A little close, but—good shooting."

Canley came in, a couple of hours later, with a few more prisoners, grinning his congratulations.

"No casualties," he said. "None to speak of anyway, except for that arm of yours."

"The arm's nothing," Bradding said. "Nothing at all. Old Bull-face here is much worse off." He indicated the recumbent chief, who was resting more on account of the bindings which fastened him to the stretcher than of the wound which had brought him down.

"Ah, but he had that from one of his friends," Canley pointed out. "We're not accountable. He looks something of a rogue."

"He's a brave man," Bradding said. "He didn't run."

"You won't misunderstand me," Canley said, "if I comment on the fact that you didn't either. And you came face to face with your enemy at last."

"It wasn't a fair test," Bradding said, frowning. "I was much too busy to do anything else. You can't tell how a man will act. There's no way of saying. But I wouldn't have had time to do anything except what I did."

Canley looked over into the distance and permitted himself a grin. "Come to think of it," he said, "I don't suppose you ever will."

The Proconsuls

*T*HE first emissary of civilization, penetrating the primeval world at the head of his long file of police and porters, encounters or creates problems of immediacy which can be resolved, and frequently have been, by qualities of courage, resource and quick thinking, strengthened by a familiarity with similar situations. Failure is not necessarily final; and failure indeed has been far more frequent than tomorrow's historian will estimate from the records. The suicide of Christopher Robinson, an early Administrator, was undoubtedly due to the aftereffects of some ghastly reprisals he conducted on a native tribe in which he substituted the principles of mass slaughter for those of justice.

But success has been so consistent as to crown with a deserved reputation for bravery the organization of District Officers. In the main they have been able to solve the early problems of contact. But these are elementary compared with those which arise after contact has become commonplace. Prominent among the latter are the movements, the influences or the beliefs which are grouped under the generic term, Cargo Cult.

It has been the fashion for newspaper writers especially to describe each manifestation of Cargo Cult as the outbreak of a new religion, and they indulge in lighthearted articles which prove this to be simply a creed conceived in muddled stupidity and centered

113

on the wishful hope that some day a ship laden with cargo is going to arrive out of the blue to the great benefit of the New Believers. The writers ascribe this silly superstition to various influences, mostly of recent origin. Australian and American reporters have lately blamed the wartime generosity of American troops for the belief, not realizing that Cargo Cult, under various other names— Vailalla Madness, Peliau Madness, Marching Rule—has been a recurrent, though happily sporadic, influence in New Guinea affairs for many years.

But the significance of the cult is much greater. The evidence must be examined in the knowledge of native logic. Natives see fallacies in European thinking; their own processes are so simple as often to be immaculate; even though the original premises of their arguments can be absurdly wide of the mark.

The truth is that the impact of the emissaries of a civilized race upon a primitive people will always produce sparks which, fattened by simple human frailties such as envy and greed, will ignite the touchy tinder of the collective mind to turn it into the conflagration of a new religion.

This is not peculiar to the South Pacific. In Kenya, Mau Mau flared into an orgy of blood-letting. In the Middle East, round two thousand years ago, the impact of the Roman legions upon the indigenes laid the foundation for the rapid development and growth of Christianity. God could not have been expected to sow His seed upon infertile ground; and the ground was prepared by the impact.

And it may be cogently pointed out that while, in the light of history, there is little doubt about the merit of that particular efflorescence, Administrator Pontius Pilate found the circumstance at least as troublesome as do the present-day administrators of the Islands and the African territories.

It was inevitable that the civilized invaders of New Guinea and the Islands should choose servants from among the happy, eager, questioning individuals that formed the native population; and that the most desirable responses should come, in a rather greater percentage than one normally finds among servants, from those intelligent, introspective members of the community who like to find things out for themselves.

Such a man finds himself in daily contact with miracles in his new surroundings. Because of his nature he is already familiar with the materials of the world he knows, and plastics, glass, refined metals, canned heat and kerosene are not among them. He recognizes only two worlds—the world he inhabits and the world to come. If the drinking glass, the silver cigarette-case or the sporting rifle he frequently handles is not of his world, then it must belong to the world of the spirits, which his dead ancestors now inhabit.

This is a simplification of the conclusions at which he arrives; but he arrives anyway at the point where the most urgently desirable thing in the world is what has been rudely described as "pie in the sky," or the Resurrection in Our Own Time.

Such a man will, when he returns to the ways of his village, and if he is capable, become a messiah of a New Order of which, if his comprehension is dim, his evangelism is moving and sincere. He talks in parables to camouflage the gaps in his knowledge, and because his experience has been enlarged beyond that of his fellows, he acquires a following. In general the following is content, at first, to ask the ancestors who inhabit the lands of wealth to send of their plenty. The example is always before them of the white man whose wealth, and to a certain extent whose skills, are not of the natural world. With the proper feasts and ceremonies they bring their requests to the attention of the spirits.

And they prepare a reception for the goods, for their faith is strong. In coastal districts where they have seen the white man's ships they build wharves to berth similar ships which, they hope,

*their ancestors will send them, loaded to the Plimsolls with the de-
sired goods. At Vailalla in Papua extensive wharves leaned drunkenly over a few inches of water that covered the river mud, and
there continued to lean for many years, far beyond the reach of
even shallow-draught shipping.*

*An old ruffian on the Rai coast west of Madang, having observed
the ways of the white man over many years, built a great shed,
an imitation Customs shed that would control and bottle-neck the
goods arriving from Heaven. He had noticed that some white men
were wealthier than others, and for himself, in the dawning day of
the brown man, he wanted a major share of tangible wealth. Therefore he proposed to control the Customs.*

*In mountain districts where ships are never seen but aircraft now
are commonplace, sweating natives constructed airfields for the
celestial gift-bearers, some of them full-size, and perfectly capable
of sustaining light traffic. In still other districts, natives agreed that
the goods would be lowered on a long rope from the sky.*

*It is important to remember that in no instance did one of these
cults give rise to another. Each was evolved spontaneously. There
are five hundred languages in New Guinea, and only recently
has there been much communication of intelligence from one tribe
to another.*

*At Vailalla again, in the early 'thirties of this century, all pre-
cautions were taken by the natives that the ships would not arrive
unheralded, and every village had its "wireless." At a listening-post
near the outskirts of each settlement, thin vines led up from a table
to the foliage of a tall tree. At the lower end of each pair of vines
was fastened a pair of half-coconut shells, and at all hours of the
day and night a native sat with a shell clamped to each ear, listening for the first tidings of the first ship.*

*In that outbreak the villagers expected the ship to be under the
command of three mysterious white men, and when they arrived,*

all natives were to become white. Only later were the three officially identified with God the Father, God the Son and the Holy Ghost, and connected with the ecstatic promises of the local missionary, a junior but enthusiastic member of his sect. In honor of the Three White Men feasts were laid out at stated periods on long trestle tables, and whenever possible these were overturned on the orders of courageous but unsympathetic patrol officers.

During comparable periods there is not, perhaps, a great deal of danger to white men. But Vailalla Madness needs results. And so does Cargo Cult. And so do all cults in the embryo period.

"My father was a good man who loved me," argues the local messiah. "And his father loved him, and the father of his father. If, then, my ancestors do not send to me the gifts which are in such quantity, there must be a reason."

Perhaps, he thinks, the ancestors do not realize how essential the new wealth is to modern living. Quite logically, therefore, the adherents of the new order burn their villages, chop down the coconut palms, burn the fences, slaughter the last pigs and dig up the last garden produce for one enormous, uproarious feast. When the ancestors realize they are quite poor, they will replace the vanished gifts of earth with the treasures of Heaven. In this there is a distinct relationship to Bible teaching, which might underline the excellence of native logic.

The cargo still does not arrive, and this ushers in the dangerous stage. In searching for a reason the leader may drop upon the notion that the white man's ancestors are preventing the brown man's ancestors from channeling the goods in the right direction. For the white man, too, has his ancestors, and they must be working very hard to see that the white man maintains such a dominant position on the earth. At this stage a visiting white man's skin would not be worth very much in the village. Lest he see the prep-

arations to receive the cargo he may be killed to prevent him from reporting to his ancestors.

This may seem a contradiction, for dead, he would, of course, be in direct touch with his ancestors. But he can be killed slowly and ceremoniously, and due magical precautions taken to see that his spirit is confined to the dead flesh. In some districts a strip of bark wrapped loosely round his body will suffice for that.

If there are plenty of white men in the district, there is always the chance of a general uprising.

In dealing with such emergencies, the Government men, showing unlimited courage, have played a strong hand. They have interrupted the feasts and the hut-burnings and imprisoned the leaders. To deal strongly with five hundred or a thousand people influenced by religious fervor when you are a lonely representative of your race, and backed by perhaps six impressionable (though dependable) natives armed with rifles is an unnerving experience. Still, it has been done, and done consistently. At Vailalla it took four years of such action to eradicate the trouble, and that time was remarkably short. On Manus Island in the Admiralties Peliau Madness ran its course for years, originated, fomented and fanned by an ex-sergeant of police, a courageous and clever native with a taste for power and a contempt of punishment. He and his creed are still alive on Manus.

The Jon Frum Movement in the New Hebrides was triggered off by a missionary indiscretion, specifically, by promises of specialized education made and not kept. In their dissatisfaction the converts to Christianity defected, and announced spiritual allegiance to an apparently mythical figure they called Jon Frum. Jon Frum, with or without a shipload of cargo, was coming, they believed, to the island of Tanna. And from there this religion followed the course of all unapproved religions, with the normal variants. There were secret meetings in this one, for instance; not feasts laid out for all to see in the village squares, but revival meetings of a sort in the forests at night, where under normal circumstances no natives would be found—not at any rate in the seasons in which the Jon Frum meetings were held. At these meetings, secret voices harangued the gathered trembling crowds from behind tree trunks.

Jon Frum, when he came, was to be a black man. And his movement was aided strongly, though perhaps unconsciously, by members of an American Negro regiment stationed in the New Hebrides during the war years in which the movement was born. Misunderstanding the stage of development Melanesians had reached, the dark Americans frequently counseled the natives to throw off the shackles of the white man. A strong factor in preventing the further development of the Jon Frum Cult was the well-developed trust and friendship the natives entertained for certain individual members of the Government service which administered their daily lives.

Jon Frum turned out to be John the Baptist, chosen for some reason that will probably never be satisfactorily explained. And Jon was going to come with his broom (in pidgin English, "frum") to sweep the "Jesus missionaries" and all other white men into the sea.

It is futile and wrong to blame, as some traders and Government officials have blamed, the missionaries and their creeds for this and similar aberrations of the native mind. The cause comes earlier, in the first impact of the white man. But in destroying the native conception of a tangible afterworld close at hand, the missionary, too, has played his little part in the evolution of these cults. For just as the Greeks believed that Mount Olympus, a tangible and neighboring territory, was the home of the gods, so the Melanesian and Polynesian religions, similarly polytheistic in general, set aside for the afterworld a territory known to their adherents.

Sometimes it is a near-by mountain, or perhaps an island the believer can reach by canoe. When he dies, the believer knows the direction he must take to reach Paradise. He is familiar with the way. He has no worries. Missionaries destroy this conception without replacing it with a compact, tangible afterworld which, after death, the native can find by following well-rehearsed directions. When the native, especially the elder native, loses this surety of knowledge he becomes bewildered, and apt to grasp at straws.

The pattern of the establishment of the Jon Frum movement was different from that of Cargo Cult, but the first important breakaway factor was the same. And that factor was the receptivity of the minds of the people, and the receptivity was brought about by the impact of the white man and his goods and chattels. His lares and penates proved greater in their influence than his Joves and Jupiters.

In the aggregate, are such religions to be taken seriously? A few lives have been lost, and a more than ample vengeance has been exacted. The people themselves have been the greatest sufferers. They have lost, for a time, the products of their gardens, and for a time lived close to starvation. Nevertheless in view of the potential capacity for harm inherent in the religions, the answer seems to be that they have not, so far, been taken seriously enough, and that good fortune has been to some degree instrumental in averting the greatest dangers.

New Guinea is, after all, a strategic area in any wartime. And in wartime, through Cargo Cult and its heating of the blood, an enemy could establish a fifth column of unbelievable ferocity. If the Japanese had but known it, there were districts in which a shipload of gew-gaws and the flat unequivocal statement: "We are your ancestors" would have won an immediate and—for the invader— a bloodless victory. There will be other enemies.

Nor in peacetime is the danger of a bloody uprising completely remote, as Mau Mau has demonstrated very convincingly in Africa.

The form of the religion, the cult or the witchcraft does not matter. The results must be averted.

The only lasting solution is the establishment of factories in the country itself. New Guinea is a land of high mountains and heavy rainfall, hence of potentially cheap hydroelectric power. It also possesses a splendid supply of factory labor and an almost untouched reservoir of raw materials. Manufacture should prove profitable as well as an educative influence. For when the processes of the modern magic become a part of daily life, the mysticism engendered and fanned by the community leaders will probably run in more conventional and acceptable channels. Copra is a commonplace. Soap is a mystery. And surely it is more profitable to ship the finished soap over the world than to pay freight charges on the bulkier raw materials taken for processing elsewhere.

But manufacture, depending as it will upon the plentiful hydroelectric power not yet tapped, will not come for years. During the last war, when the real menace of Cargo Cult was at its most pressing, other measures had to be attempted.

The cheapest, the quickest and the one most likely to succeed lay in shipping a number of village representatives to the centers of manufacture on the Australian mainland, and letting them see the processes for themselves. This was done. Australian army authorities tried to insure that at least two boys from each village in danger areas were selected. They came and they saw. They were escorted through glass-making works and textile mills, and their general level of education was trebled and quadrupled in a matter of weeks. When the representatives were returned to their villages, the venture proved to have been only partially successful at best.

For the village elders had logic and reasoning beyond the imagination of the civilized planners. Not unnaturally, the choice of representatives had been selective, and the chosen were young men of quick intelligence and good health. It was, perhaps, the only

*possible choice. Old men were too hard to convince, too set in their
habits of thought.*

*But when the young men returned and tried to correct their
elders, there was an immediate and strong revulsion from what
they had to say. And the elders had a good argument against anything at all they might happen to be told. It was addressed to the
others in the village councils, and it ran like this:*

*"The white man took Wageru away in the big ship, and week
after week ran round after Wageru, and spent his time in entertain-
ing him. And white women fed Wageru and looked after him. The
white people have done a great deal for Wageru, and all they have
asked of him is that he come back here to his village and tell us
this tale. They have not asked him to work, to fetch and carry, or
to return gift for gift.*

*"But the white man must have something to make of it. It seems
to me the white man did all this for Wageru because he was afraid
for the safety of the great wealth that comes to him from his ancestors. He is afraid lest we, the brown people, find the source of
the white man's wealth and power. And so he took Wageru, who is
young, and therefore easily deceived, and showed him many marvels. And even if Wageru saw what he says he saw, there was magic
in the showing. For Wageru says that glass is but earth and ashes
burned in a fire, and we know this is not true. If this were true all
the world would be glass where the campfires have burned. It is
a thing to laugh at. If I thought before that the white men were
anxious to hide the sources of their wealth, now I am certain."*

*Wageru can talk all he wants to about the mighty furnaces and
the massive machinery, and the thousands of white wen who work
with their hands. In politeness his neighbors will believe that he
thought he saw it all. They will believe he had a dream about this,
or that a huge and complicated show was staged purely to deceive*

him. But they will not believe the essential truth of what he has to say.

And it is logical that they do not. The whole drama of these nascent religions lies in their irrefutable logic, built up, of course, from wrong premises.

Cargo cults have also arisen in circumstances in which the Administration did not see its duty so clearly. There was a fairly recent example in the D'Entrecasteaux Islands. In this place an anthropologist had been engaged in whatever it is that engages anthropologists; and an elderly native lady, long past the age for child-bearing, made an announcement that she and the anthropologist had been chosen by God to begin a new race, the members of which would lead the people of New Guinea to everlasting happiness. She said it convincingly; perhaps on the authority of dreams, perhaps from a mistaken conception of the import of things she had been told. The anthropologist decided that work on the mainland, and, shortly afterward, in another hemisphere, was of greater urgency than that which had lately engaged him, and the whole outburst fizzled out in an unsatisfactory way.

The ground was prepared, however, and in the same district today another woman is at the head of the local variety of Cargo Cult. She talks to the stump of a tree and from it she receives directions which she transmits to her numerous followers. She could become dangerous. But she is the mistress of an aging white trader, ex-missionary helper; and she is not arrested, her preaching is left unchecked because to interfere with her would also interfere with the old man's comfort.

This is the working of a double standard of law. Natives are arrested for a great many offenses which may be committed with careless impunity by white men; and the educated among the indigenes do not like it. As an example, a native may be jailed for seven years for setting foot at night in a house where a white woman lives, no matter what his motive.

There is a law too which forbids the unmarried white man to have native women in his house at night, or even to spend the night under the same roof. But on a coral island of storied romance I once stayed with the beachcomber-planter-trader for a brief afternoon. There was a little company of us—the beachcomber, a banker, a schooner skipper, a Government representative and myself. We stirred our tea with spoons which left the flavor of ancient cod-liver-oil in the brew, and listened to a great deal of talk about the dirty amorality of the thieving natives. Only there was nothing on that island for natives to steal. By inheritance they owned it all. The water supply of the natives was dipped from shallow holes scraped in the beach sand each morning. In forty years the beachcomber had not even sunk a barrel for the benefit of the tribes he ruled as a kind of unofficial king.

Late at night, the banker and I left to sleep on one of the ships lying off the beach. But the skipper and the Government man stayed behind. For their delectation, as of long habit, the beachcomber had produced a bevy of eleven little girls who, as we went, were huddled yawning on the floor.

The shocking feature was in the age of the girls, of whom only one was more than half-grown, or of sufficient physical development to have any breasts at all. She was the housekeeper. She was aged about sixteen and I would estimate the age of the others at no more than nine or ten.

The Government representative in that party was not the first to enjoy the favors of this constantly changing stable. It was a matter for lively speculation when, after the war, this beachcomber was permitted to return to his island almost two years before other residents were allowed to take up the threads of their island lives.

You may rub shoulders with men in New Guinea who have committed worse crimes (if you admit that there are worse crimes); and talk about them without fear. This establishment of the double standard is one of the greatest weaknesses of Government, and productive of an ever-increasing number of problems.

Another great difficulty the Government has made for itself, and this time with its eyes open, has been in the destruction of the old community laws. They had to go. Their penalties were death and torture; their prestige was based upon the sacrifice of human life. But their regimen was strict, and the people under their jurisdiction were disciplined. If the destruction of the laws could have been contemporaneous with a new education, so that the new regime could have been understood and appreciated, the Government could have anticipated little trouble. But education is still woefully inadequate, and the country lacks the instruments for education, the schools and the teachers.

Self-education in the ways of civilization is debarred from a people who, in practice, are confined to their own land because of the working of the White Australia policy, an outmoded but carefully policed Australian economic measure. Only under special circumstances and then under a strict control may a few carefully selected youngsters visit Australia and see civilization in action.

Education has been further restricted by the widespread adoption of two master-slave languages, police Motu and pidgin English; but today some ineffective attempts are being made to provide the people with education in English, a rather more adequate means of communication.

The development of the country will mean a wholesale shifting of populations. Thousands upon thousands of natives have already left their village homes for the mines, the plantations, and for the larger ports; and while regulations provide that, when their period of employment has come to an end, they must be returned to their homes, large numbers of them stay of their own free will, or, from the village, find their way back again. It was a responsibility of the Government officer, in the old days, to see that too much manpower was not recruited from any one village; that sufficient men of active age were left to work the gardens and the fishing-grounds, and that too heavy a responsibility should not rest upon the women, the children and the aged.

The intervention of the United Nations has had unhappy results here. It is held, under the "Freedom to Work" ideal, that if a man wishes to leave his village he may do so. In the implementation of this ideal it is frequently forgotten that while man is undoubtedly due a freedom to work, a freedom of choice in his job is, in all communities, conditioned by the amount and type of work available. It seems wrong to insist on the individual's freedom of choice at the expense of the welfare of his dependents. And this is only one instance of many in New Guinea in which a worthy ideal plays havoc with orderly development.

Labor shortage is today on the side of the "Freedom" pundits; and the old control over the village has been relinquished, along with other regulations. There was an old law, for example, that forbade the wearing of clothes above the waist by natives. It was a good law, and responsible in large measure for maintaining health standards; but it was inevitable that it should some day be relinquished.

The Administrator often makes problems for himself, too, by treating symptoms instead of diseases, after the manner of a majority of the unlettered practitioners in the New Guinea medical services. For example, in one district where, in contrast to most of the land, a native aristocracy was installed, a District Officer decided to vest the peasants under his control with the ownership of many pigs and many coconut palms. Previously these amenities and all others had been the property of the chiefs. Since that date his successors have spent a great deal of time working on litigation affecting ownership.

It is almost an understatement to affirm that all the problems inherent in the people and their logic increase with increased contact; and so do the problems raised by Administration; by an increasing army of administrators. Increasing friction is inevitable, and it will continue until the problems of the primitive are altogether overcome and swamped by the problems of the civilized.

And here one must ask whether, in fact, the basic problems are so very different. The impact of new materials and new processes has thrown up the troublesome cults of the awakening New Guinea; and in the world outside the widest publicity has been given to the new processes and materials of the Atom Age. And we, too, have had our prophets and our messiahs: the people who have seen the portents in the sky. We, too, have, to some extent, become obsessed with the imagined possibilities of worlds beyond the world; we have awaited the landing of the Flying Saucer, sometimes with the same intensity as the people in the villages have looked to the coming of the Ship Full of Cargo.

Is it possible that, looking toward Cargo Cult, we can evaluate the real menace, the mental menace, of nuclear fission? Does it threaten us with the uncontrollable fervors of a sweeping new religion? Or perhaps, is its beneficent function to prepare the mind of civilized man for the acceptance of some new and powerful belief? . . . or for a demonstrable and necessary variation in his current beliefs? . . . or for a homogeneous molding of the thousand and one beliefs of today into one creed based on recognizable and acceptable truths?

The lesson of Cargo Cult is that the atom bomb and the new discoveries of science, when they are applied to the domestic lives of the nations, will intensify metaphysical thinking. New religions will certainly arise, and new interest in older religions. Whether these developments will be good or bad will depend upon the character of the men who seize upon the moment.

The Wisdom
of Ragos

I N the village of Sagintip the old man they
called Ragos was neither rich nor poor, neither
proud nor humble, neither clever nor stupid.
He had no great influence on the council, yet the councilors
listened to his opinion. He had no great capacity for work, yet
people enlisted his help for a house building or a hunt. He was
neither good nor bad; a good neighbor who quarreled sometimes;
a good husband who nagged sometimes. He came to new ideas with
reluctance yet sometimes he was impatient with the old ways too.
Life was good to him, and the people of Sagintip were kind, and he
had met with little trouble until the day he married the girl Tamea.

Yet Tamea was a good wife for him, strong and healthy and eager
to work. She was just a young girl, but she was tall and well formed.
When she walked her limbs were loose like the limbs of a baby who
rides on its mother's neck. She was strong and could carry two
head-nets filled with yams for hours and not tire, even though they
were so heavy she had to swing them to her back one at a time.
She was a good fisherwoman, and she tended her garden very well
without instructions from Ragos.

She was good-looking too, and before her marriage she might

have commanded a bride-price beyond the ability of Ragos to pay, except for a little thing. She was a flirt. The women said she was a wanton.

She smiled at the men all day, and giggled and laughed. She would break off any conversation while a man was passing and watch him out of sight in the hope that he might make a sign to her. When men passed and other women sat still, Tamea moved. If the other women were on the move, Tamea was standing still. Her voice was shriller than the rest. And though of course none of the men appeared to take notice of Tamea in a group of women, many of them made a mental note to pass that way again when the others might have gone. And many of them found, in fact, that Tamea had been delayed.

Even when she was a little girl with her first skirt she was thinking of men. Sometimes when she sat by herself she would take a stick and wrap it round with a leaf, and talk to it, pretending it was a man.

After she was married to Ragos she didn't act as the other girls did and mend her ways; and she became only a little more discreet; but people said nothing to her husband because they were kindly, and they wished her well just as they wished well to Ragos. But when Ragos found her in adultery with the youth Rangiap then they chuckled and told stories about her, and laughed at Ragos because, now that they pitied him a little, they held him in less esteem.

How they laughed when Ragos beat Tamea! He took a good stick and beat Tamea soundly, and shouted at her until all the village knew her shame. He was a very angry man and he tried to teach Tamea a lesson.

But what should he do about Rangiap? Ragos was a man between two worlds. In his time the white man had stopped the taking of heads, and cleared away the skulls from the carved meeting-house. With the skulls the white man had taken the power from the village council. The old men could discipline the youths no longer. The laws and the matters of moment were no longer in their hands. There was no clear-cut path for Ragos to follow.

So when his anger had cooled a little he sat on the steps of his house and waited. Presently Tinga, the headman, came along, and Ragos made him a sign and spoke to him, and Tinga joined him on the porch of the house. Ragos sent the weeping Tamea to work, and she went with downcast head; but she looked even then, with dancing eyes, at the youths who had gathered at the edge of the clearing when they had first heard the noise of the beating. And soon to the house came Barova and Tauni and the old, old man they called Dikdik; and others who were in the council; and Ragos told them his problem.

They sat and smoked a long time in the early morning sunlight, and presently Tinga said, "The Government will have a law. This is Government business. Tomorrow take your wife, Tamea, and the man Rangiap and go to the house of Master Steven at Kuwadi, and Master Steven will have an answer. You must take the man and the woman and ask Master Steven for a court, because this is the right way, the way of Government."

Presently, too, the others, Tauni and Barova and the old and wrinkled man they called Dikdik, took the cigarettes from their mouths to agree, though Dikdik sighed heavily, remembering the days that were past, with their swift and heavy punishments, and their rare transgressions.

So the following day Ragos and Rangiap, with the woman Tamea behind them, walked along the track to the village at Kuwadi, on the outskirts of which the Administration had built a house and set up the district office.

District Officer Jerry Stevens was living alone at Kuwadi. His wife had not returned from the furlough on which he had sent her to Australia six months before, and in this same week a letter from her, written at length and carefully unemotional, had told him what everyone else in the Territory had suspected before him: that she never intended coming back. Outwardly he showed no trace of the considerable storm the letter had raised in him, for he was a sober man and knew his responsibilities to his district. Inwardly he felt lost and forlorn; but above all he felt ashamed.

This difficulty, of course, was aggravated by living alone, and by the fact that his contacts with other white men were casual and infrequent. But he clung rather desperately to that same loneliness, being afraid, not so much of his friends as of his acquaintances. He could hear, for instance, the fellows in the New Guinea bar in Usher's Hotel in Sydney talking about it. Pitying him.

"Poor old Jerry," they would say. "Hasn't been the same man since Evelyn walked out on him. Buried himself at Kuwadi and he's staying there."

It wouldn't be so much what they said as what they left unsaid; their feeling that he had been played for a sucker, some tacit understanding that he was deficient in some male qualities. Even the friendly barmaid, Madge, would have heard some echoes of some of the stories. She knew everything that was anything in New Guinea. He felt he couldn't go back there for a drink if he wanted to. And Sydney could be a lonely place.

He might have been content to believe that no one knew about his troubles except for the other letter, the unexpected communication from the Administrator's office suggesting an unexpected and almost immediate furlough. His time was overdue; but he knew the service was understaffed; and while he appreciated the consideration that he was extended, he resented that his superiors should apparently be aware of his difficulties. The mail wouldn't go out for a fortnight, the radio was out of commission—he could take his time. He decided against going anywhere; he would stay on the job and forget, if he could, that there was anything anywhere for which he could be pitied.

And he would try to think of Evelyn in the new, impersonal disguise she had assumed in the letter; not cruel or wanton, but remote, as though her light and brilliant gaiety had drowned in some cool stillness.

In the meantime he had his work, and by it he was fascinated. He could lose himself in the variety of his problems. In his hands was the development of twelve or fifteen thousand people, little brown men whose fathers had practiced head-hunting and ruled their fellows and themselves with fear and blood spilling. His was the task of softening for them the new fears and sorrows engendered by their contact with a new way of life. He was bringing them gently to civilized ways of thought, staying the headlong rush of the younger men to embrace the new ideas, encouraging the oldsters to go along. For himself he would have preferred to leave the people the way they were before the missionary and the trader found them. He was too late; a hundred years too late. All he could do was to keep the pace of their development within their capabilities. Stevens was a good officer.

There was, however, as he realized, another danger for him in this devotion to his work. He was sufficient of a psychologist to know, without bringing it to words, that unless he had some basis of comparison; unless he identified himself with the people of his own race in their own surroundings at reasonably frequent intervals, he could lose his sense of perspective, and without perspective he would be valueless. He was in process of making a rather dismal evaluation of his personal function in the world.

On this morning he had made his inspection of the grounds and the police barracks and was deciding against a visit to the native hospital (presided over by a bright native youngster with twelve months' medical schooling) when three figures emerged from the track leading to the village. They were natives who did not have much to draw the attention, and he thought idly he might have seen them in one of the district villages, but he could not place them. They were not bush natives, because all three wore cloth lap-laps, but they did not come from any of the nearer villages under his care, because the lap-laps were dirty.

The leader was an old man, straight enough and possessed of a certain dignity. He wore great wooden plugs in his ear lobes, and his arms were braceleted. In his right hand he held the wrist of a young fellow with a cheeky grin, and he was leading him as though he held him in custody. The young fellow could have broken away at any moment. Instead he acted as though he were enjoying a great public joke, and Stevens immediately took a dislike to him.

Behind the two came a tall girl with loose, gangling limbs—"Lolly-legs," Stevens said to himself. Like the youth, she was dressed in a cloth lap-lap, and from her head a large carrying bag, nearly empty, swung and lolloped gently on her back with the loose action of her own muscles. The girl walked with downcast head, but she looked cheekily at Stevens below her lashes, and he could have smacked her for the invitation in her eyes.

The old man tendered a greeting which Stevens returned. The language was a "place-talk," a village language which Stevens recognized, but with which he was not familiar. He knew and spoke well two of the four place-talks spoken in his district as well as the lingua franca. He also had a working knowledge of several tongues spoken in districts in which he had formerly been stationed. He tried the old man with the lingua franca, but obviously it was unintelligible to him. The younger man, however, replied fluently.

"I am Rangiap," he said. "This old man is Ragos, and we come from the village of Sagintip. He has come to ask you for a court."

"Tell him then to follow me," Stevens said, and turned abruptly on his heel. He had no intention of allowing the accused to put his

own, presumably plausible, tale; or to twist the old man's accusa-
tions. He sent a naked little brown youngster running for a police
boy of his named Colin, a reliable interpreter of the Sagintip talk.

When Colin had heard the old man's story he retailed it to Stevens.

"Sir," he said, "this man is called Ragos and the woman is
Tamea, his wife. He says he caught her in adultery with the man
Rangiap. He has brought them in and he asks you for a court."

Stevens looked at Rangiap, and the youth smiled openly. "Truly
the old man caught us," he said.

"Ask the woman," Stevens directed Colin.

Tamea smiled delightedly when the police boy spoke to her, and
her eyes twinkled. She talked animatedly back, nodding her head.

"The woman says it is true," said Colin.

"Then I will hold a court," Stevens told him. "This afternoon
at two o'clock. See that they are there."

The court was set outside, near the flag gracing the miniature
parade ground where Stevens held such ceremonies as seemed to
him fitting to impress the natives. He adhered closely to the visual
forms of Government, realizing that his people stood in need of
temporal leadership more and more, and would continue thus until such time as they could regain a spiritual inspiration. Their
own religious observances had been broken, and had ceased to
mean much to them; and the replacement by Christianity was still
only partly understood.

The court consisted of a table and chair set out in the shade
furnished by a little group of eucalypts at the edge of the parade
ground. Behind the trees was a hedge of manioc, overlooked by
pink temple-flowers and brilliant hibiscus. There was a Bible on
the table, and several other books, along with official forms and
pen and ink.

"Rangiap of Sagintip, the old man Ragos has charged you with wife-stealing," Stevens said, the term giving a better conception of wrongdoing than any other synonym for adultery.

Ragos gave his evidence with a great show of indignation, and Stevens, looking behind this, and hearing only sounds of which the meaning would presently come to him through the interpreter, could see that he had been really hurt. Probably an earlier wife, consistently faithful, had made him happy, Stevens thought. But when the translation came, if he could believe it to be the whole truth, it seemed that Ragos had no direct sense of personal loss through finding his wife, Tamea, with the youth. It was his dignity that had suffered, for his talk was all of the effect of the discovery upon the other people of the village.

"He says, moreover," Colin was translating, "that the people of the village now laugh at him. The young men laugh from a distance, and the women giggle when he goes by. He says Rangiap has greatly harmed his standing."

Stevens grunted and looked down at the papers he had assembled on the table to give standing to the proceedings. There was a parallel here to himself, and he felt embarrassed, remembering how even at that moment he was shrinking from the thought of meeting the boys in the New Guinea bar, or, at closer hand, in the clubs of the main settlements, for that matter. He looked up at the woman and she was dimpling her face at Colin while her husband's attention was elsewhere. An old man like Ragos could never hold a wench like that, Stevens thought.

It was an open-and-shut case. Rangiap admitted to his misdemeanor altogether too cheerfully, and Stevens spoke sharply to him. His evidence was corroborated by the woman, who hung her head and clasped one broad foot over the other as she spoke.

"Now this is a very serious charge, Rangiap," Stevens said, "and I find you guilty of it. Wife-stealing is no light thing, nothing to make a joke about because a wife is the greatest of the possessions of Ragos, and if a wife is not to be trusted she is no wife. Nevertheless a woman is weak and a man should see that she sticks to her trust. You have done a great hurt to Ragos who can no longer hold his head up in Sagintip. An old man's head should be at rest at nights and his heart happy.

"Therefore I am going to fine you a pound for wife-stealing," he said impressively. There was a little gasp among the people who had come to watch the court, the sergeant and the two police boys on duty, the little group of women squatting under the tree, the children crowding shyly together, the seven or eight men from the village, and the other prisoners—five miscreants who had been playing at cards. A pound was a whole month's wages; not a fortune, but a stiff fine.

"And in default," Stevens said, "that is to say if the pound is not paid, then you will go to prison for a month."

The people looked impressed again, all except the plaintiff, Ragos, and his wife, Tamea, to whom the talk was foreign. The man Rangiap hung his head and looked down at his feet.

"Have you anything to say?" Stevens asked him.

He looked up. "Master, I have not got the money."

"Then you will go to prison for a month," Stevens said cheerfully. He could always find work for another prisoner, looking after the garden, cutting the grass, repairing the jeep road.

The old man was talking, jabbering away directly at Stevens, who could not understand.

"What does he say?" he asked Colin.

"Sir, he wants to know what has been said. He wants to know what is the word of the court."

"Then tell him," Stevens said. "It is his court. Tell him the man was fined, that he must pay a pound or go to prison for a month."

Colin spoke to Ragos, who replied.

"He says it is a wise decision and he thanks you. He asks can they all go now, because he wants to travel to the place they stopped last night before it is dark."

"Tell him he can go now," Stevens said patiently. "He and his wife can go now, but Rangiap has to go to prison."

Ragos was surprised. "Why does he not pay the money?" he asked in the place-talk. "Why does he not give the pound? He is wanted back in the village. His wife will need him."

"Rangiap does not have a pound. Rangiap must go to jail," Colin explained.

"No pound?" asked Ragos. "I have a pound." He groped below the folds of the lap-lap and produced a dirty twisted rag of green paper. Ceremoniously he unfolded it and laid it on the table.

"Here is a pound for Rangiap," he said. "Now can we go? We have a long way to walk."

"Wait," said Stevens, sitting up. "What is this?"

Colin explained. "It is a gift to Rangiap."

"No!" protested Stevens. He spoke earnestly. "This is a loan from Ragos," he said to Rangiap. "In less than two months I shall come to Sagintip. The loan will have been repaid. If any part of the pound is not repaid then the Government will take you for stealing money by fraud, and will imprison you for a month for fraud. Is this understood?"

Rangiap said, "Yes, master. I understand." He was more serious now.

Stevens motioned to Colin to translate to the others. The old man listened and spoke briefly, and Colin returned the phrase. "He thanks you. He says the Government is wise."

Stevens dismissed them, and the little group walked away, the men together. There was no longer a symbolically detaining hand round Rangiap's wrist, but they did not walk as friends. Ragos, in spite of his satisfaction, was still gloomy, and Rangiap had lost the cheerfulness with which he had arrived. Only, as they went, Tamea looked back over her shoulder, and Stevens could have sworn she was making big eyes at him until he saw that the look was for Colin.

That evening, after the ceremony of flag lowering which coincides, in those latitudes, so exactly and dramatically with the swift sunset, Stevens called the boy Colin over to him.

"You know this village, Sagintip, well?" he asked.

"Yes, sir," said Colin. "I am from Lunduana, not a long way from it. I know them fairly well in Sagintip. I know the man Rangiap, but not the girl Tamea."

"That is good," said Stevens. "I will not be pleased if you get to know her either, at least for a little while. What sort of fellow is this Rangiap?"

"Very good," said Colin. "He is well liked. It is a year and more since I have seen him, but he is popular."

"He would be," Stevens said, with a trace of bitterness, and turned away rather abruptly.

The house still bore traces of Evelyn—the carved ivory ball within a ball within another ball and other wonders from the Chinese stores in Rabaul; glass-dipped ceramics, bright and hard; a modernistic ashtray from Sydney, coarse Chinese imitations of Japanese cloisonné; nothing very substantial. All of it was now overshadowed with male litter—pipes on the occasional table, piles of magazines and books in every corner; but there was sufficient to make him think of her. And when he thought of her he kept thinking back to Ragos.

More and more in the next few weeks he thought about that particular court, a detail of his work which would have been erased from his mind on its completion had it not been for the mad little incident of the plaintiff paying the defendant's fine. Stevens tended to identify the old man's loss of prestige with his own situation; though as far as he knew there was no exact parallel, for he had no more than a strong suspicion that it was some other male responsible for his wife's alienation. But to be fair to himself, there was a distinct parallel in the girl's happy-go-lucky and random advances and his wife's more discreet but omnivorous sociability.

He funked the problem. As an addendum to his next report he wrote a note tentatively declining an immediate furlough, but leaving the matter open for the near-future. The course he took was not satisfactory to him. It was a compromise and compromises annoyed him.

But it was, consequently, with something more than idle curiosity that Stevens on his regular patrol approached the village of Sagintip just a week or two earlier than he had indicated.

Sagintip lay on an inlet of the sea almost completely choked at its entrance by the beautiful savagery of coral, and no boats could approach or lie there with safety. In spite of a position central in the district, it would remain an isolated village until the end of time, because of the steep mountain paths which were its only access.

Nevertheless it was, for native living, a rich village, well fed, with good gardens on the hillside and a wealth of fish in the sea. Moreover it was a clean village, with the houses set on stilts over carefully brushed sand, and little shell-gardens among the houses.

The water supply came from a tiny trickle on a clay bank at the edge of the white beach. It was pure spring water, but the trickle was so tiny it had to be diverted from the clay by a fresh green leaf, pressed newly into the clay each morning so that it diverted a tiny flow of water into a bamboo pipe and thence into a galvanized iron bucket. Thus, from little more than a damp patch on the bank came the drinking water for a score of houses. The matrons used the sea for washing their utensils and for water to cook their vegetables, and the seashore was always a place gay with chatter and laughter. There was always a little fleet of outrigger canoes there, drawn up on the sand. Altogether the village was a place which Stevens visited with a great deal of anticipated pleasure.

This time he was almost anxious to reach the village. However, he was disappointed with the reply to what was almost his first question, for neither the old man Ragos nor the youth Rangiap was there.

"Was the money paid?" he asked the headman, Tinga.

"Truly it is a wonder that the waster could find the money," Tinga said. "But yes, he paid it. It was a good direction of the Government. And Ragos by it has earned the respect of the people."

"How's that again?" Stevens said, surprised. "I mean, do the people give respect to Ragos because of the money?"

"They do truly," Tinga said. "And this is right, too, because Ragos came to the aid of the wife-stealer when otherwise he would have gone to prison. And so the waster is able to look after his own wife. And it has shown that Rangiap is a small man, because his hands were busy with more than he could put in his mouth."

The attitude puzzled Stevens. He asked questions throughout the village and everywhere he found the same result—a huge and increased respect for Ragos, a new contempt for Rangiap. The respect extended to himself for the judgment he had given, and this puzzled him, too, because he felt that though it had been simple and fair enough, it had had a good deal of emotion behind it, too. He had felt guilty about that emotion, engendered by his own matrimonial troubles. The people were right, he felt. But he was surprised that this should have been their reaction.

Late in the day, when he had finished his business in the village, Colin came to him.

"There is something about this business of Ragos that you don't know," he said. "I think I should tell you, if you would like to hear."

"What is it?" Stevens asked.

"Sir: the money for the fine. It belonged to Tinga, the headman, and not to Ragos. Tinga lent it to Ragos to bring it to the court so that he should be prepared. Tinga said that there would be a fine of money, and that it would be a good thing if Ragos held the money."

"Well, I'm damned," said Stevens. He laughed, and Colin looked at him inquiringly. "Sir?" he asked.

"There is no blame in that," said Stevens. "Tinga is a wise man."

Colin started to walk away and as he did so the sleepy afternoon was broken by another movement in the village. On a near-by veranda a woman stretched herself, yawned vigorously and stood up. She reached for a fish-spear that leaned against the wall, and with it walked down the little ladder onto the brushed sand. As she turned the corner of the house and walked toward the sea, Stevens noted the loose action of the lolly-legs and saw that it was Tamea. He saw, too, that she was looking over her shoulder and smiling; and, looking in the direction of the smile, he saw the solemn face of Colin. He beckoned, and Colin came back to him.

"I don't think it would be a good idea to get to know the wife of Ragos any better," he said, directly.

"No, sir," said Colin. "Nor do I." He watched the figure of Tamea as she waited, knee-deep in the gentle surf, with the spear upraised and waiting for a fish. The tide had just turned, and the banks of coral farther out lay like solid rock on the waters. Soon the armies of fish would sweep in, chasing close to the beach to find the wealth of food that had been caught and sun-killed in the ebb's recession of the waters.

"Yet she is a woman a man might look at twice," Colin added pensively. Then his face brightened. "But we are close to my village of Lunduana," he said. "Perhaps we sleep at Lunduana tomorrow?"

"Yes, Colin," Stevens said. "Tomorrow we sleep at Lunduana."

"That's good, sir. I have friends at Lunduana."

"Women friends, Colin?" Stevens asked.

"I know some women," Colin replied.

He looked straight in Stevens' eye and grinned hugely. "The

women of Lunduana are small and quick, and very gay," he said. "They are better than the women of Sagintip who are slow and stupid. Yes, I know some women," he repeated. "I am sure there are women at Lunduana who remember me."

Stevens dismissed him and asked no more questions. He felt that some mild reproof was in order, but he didn't have the heart to give it. And besides, he had made his own resolves, mapped out his own plan of action, and he wanted to think about it. For the first time in months he was thinking about himself and being happy. He would accept the furlough which was on offer—he could still do it. And he would go to Sydney and meet his problems and face the people of his own world again, steering a direct course; because after all it was the judgment of his fellows that he had been evading. He was sure he could win his Evelyn back and find a solution to his future; and he felt grateful to Ragos who had shown him the way. He felt grateful to Tinga, too, who used his wisdom to help his people; and in a larger sense he felt that with his own response, by applying the lessons of the village to his own world, by enlarging the scope of Tinga's wisdom, he could in some small measure repay him.

The Village
of Phantom Ships

KUDGIL sat facing the river on the platform of
the House Tamboran, but his eyes were on the
village, so that he caught the first glimpse of
Talua when she came stooping through the low-linteled doorway
of her dwelling, climbed down the crossbar steps and walked past
the houses.

Talua was beautiful. She was tall for a village girl, over five feet,
and her body was firm and well formed. Her legs were better
muscled than the thin shanks of most of the canoe people. They
carried grace and symmetry. In her close-cropped curly hair she
wore three bright yellow orchids; and between her pretty breasts
she cuddled her pet black fowl, a rooster who had lost most of his
feathers in the cause of Talua's adornment.

Kudgil loved her. He loved to watch her walk through the village,
swinging the skirt over her hips as a well-behaved woman should,
displaying its colors of rust and corn and gray. It was a full and respectable skirt that fell halfway to her knees behind, and not quite
so far in front; a skirt made with care and infinite industry from
the flower of the sago palm. A skirt that proclaimed her a wife fit
for Kudgil. But before she could be his wife there was the small

matter of the bride-price. When Talua was out of sight and there was no least chance that she would answer his look with a look, Kudgil swung round and disappeared inside the House Tamboran to count his possessions.

They made a small pile, a lonely pile in a small corner of the vast temple where the gods no longer lived, a little accumulation of bright debris nestled at the foot of one of the great carved wooden pillars that supported the central rooftree, fifty feet above his head, and four times that in length. Kudgil had never known the full terror of the House Tamboran. The missionary, some forgotten missionary, had taken away the skulls and the best of the carvings; and with them he had removed the authority vested in the building. There were still skulls beneath the massive piles that supported the rafters; and more skulls, made lifelike again with clay and paint, hidden in the joining of the rooftrees, where none could see them.

There were two fresh skulls here, that the white man must not discover; for there were still a few villagers who believed in the power that demanded skulls to back its prestige; but this was no business of Kudgil's. For him the House Tamboran, the place of the councils and the initiations was an almost empty barn, a common storehouse, a village hall, its furnishings limited to the three carved council tables, each hewn from the solid stump of a tree, and a few stools.

Kudgil squatted on the polished palmwood floor and looked at his goods, seeing them now, not as he had seen them on that glorious day of his return—the riches of a year spent working for the white man—but as a working capital that was too puny for a man with his life before him. A capital far too puny for Kudgil.

Because the bride-price for Talua was immense: six pearl shells, two shells of the green sea snail and a handful of cowries. It was a price that might bring him six women, though none of them would be Talua.

If Talua had nothing but her beauty he would not have considered buying. But Talua had more. This was a fishing village, but Talua was heiress to the best hunting valley of the tribe; and Kudgil, by preference, was a hunter. A marriage with Talua would some day bring him wealth; great wealth. A woman with fishing-rights might mean more to some suitors. But Kudgil was a hunter first; and he wanted the hunting-rights of the valley that was Talua's.

For this was the rule of the tribe: that the women owned the property, while each man controlled only that which was his wife's; and that a wife cost money. Thus the young men worked to acquire wives, and the men who had the most wives worked the hardest. And they had the most power, as was right. Wealth came, first from work and then from marriage; and marriage increased the amount of work to be done.

The wealth of Kudgil was little, though once it had seemed great enough to him. He had seven shafts of iron from the engineer's shop at the mines of Bulolo; shafts that would make him spears that would last forever. A belt of plastic and five bead armlets from the store of the Chinese trader. Four lap-laps for his wear, and a blanket for his sleep. A bush knife. Thirteen razor blades. A small water tumbler and a little bag of money. Nearly forty marks in the bag, and a paper that was twenty marks. All his wealth together would not buy six pearl shells, or if it would it would leave nothing over.

He left his treasures and went out again to the platform of the House Tamboran in the sun, where the mosquitoes did not bite so much and he could watch the deep river flowing, eddying against the piles. He sat and waited and thought of whether Gerlap, the father of Talua, would lower the bride-price for him; and he knew that Gerlap would not, at least in this year. In a harder year a wife might come cheaper.

But Kudgil had other things to think of, too; and after awhile he went in again and took the small drinking vessel of glass he had

stolen from the white man in Bulolo. And he took the paper that
was twenty marks and his bush knife for company. He untied a
canoe and paddled upriver under the shadow of the trees where the
current ran slow until he came to a landing stage. Here, in a clearing on the bank, Chu Lim, the Chinese trader, had established a
store, an outpost of trade which served the native tribes along thirty
miles of the river.

Kudgil bought one tin of bully beef for which he had no opener
and a bright red bangle of light plastic; and he came to his canoe
again and thereafter disappeared.

Of his whereabouts there was no mystery. Nobody missed him.
At least, nobody searched for him. Otherwise they could easily have
found him in the hut of a deserted garden five miles upriver from
Chu Lim's. He was so far from the village, in fact, that his life was
to some extent in danger from the not-yet-blooded youths of the
next tribe. For head-hunting was a custom not entirely forgotten,
and there was merit yet for the hunter if his exploits did not come
to the ears of Government.

In the garden, Kudgil spread new clay over the palm floorboards
of the hut for his fire, and he sat there.

He did not eat, and he spent a great deal of time with the glass,
the can of beef, and the bright bangle; yet mostly with the glass,
turning it over and over in his hands, and feeling the fine smooth
edge of it. Sometimes he rubbed it against the skin of his belly to
feel the smoothness of the glass against the tender skin. Until he
had gone with the recruiter to Bulolo there had been nothing like
the glass in his experience. It did not come from the sea or the river
or the rocks of the mountain. And it was bound up in its origins
with the mysterious wealth of the white man.

It was a thing not of this earth; and of the things beyond the
earth there was no knowing. But something to which it had belonged
meant wealth. And wealth meant Talua. And more wealth. And a

new life in which wealth came without work, as it came to the white men who could, if they wished, work hard, but who knew very well how not to work. Who never worked to get their food, as the brown men did. And who could keep their women without working the women.

Kudgil looked at the glass for five days. Toward each night he went about, and gathered a little wood for the fire, and green leaves to make a smudge to fight the mosquitoes; but he did not eat. Near the end of the five days he slept often, but always woke in a little while and looked at the glass. And then the great truth came to him.

He sat back on his haunches and considered this truth. It was a big truth and he looked at it carefully. But it was a solid and inescapable truth, and from it he knew it was time to return to the village. He went to a kapiak tree at the edge of the clearing and brought back a breadfruit and blew at the embers to make a flame, and put it on the fire. Then he gathered a bunch of woody bananas and scorched them, too, and ate the breadfruit and the bananas quickly. Then he took the canoe and paddled downriver to the village.

There was sufficient in what he had to tell to bring a council together. That night a man went beneath the House Tamboran with a cudgel, and beat the big garamuts. And the garamuts spoke, the drum notes carrying the message of the council over the hills and the valleys, over the country for thirty miles in every direction, and the men of the village, sleeping out in their gardens, heard the message and made themselves ready to come back with the morning light.

Kudgil did not sleep. He was tired; but there was a pain in his belly and he was excited, like a man in a small fever. But when the council came together he spoke, standing by a table in the House Tamboran and looking at the faces all about him. There were two faces that he watched more closely than the others. One was the face of Laseki who was headman below Tombarap, the luluai; and the other was the face of Gerlap, the father of Talua.

On the table beside his hand were the bright red bangle, the can of beef and the drinking glass.

Now all the men had seen these things before, or things like them; but there was something about them, and when Kudgil began to speak the men kept their eyes on the things on the table, the bangle and the can and the glass.

Kudgil said: "I've been a long way, and I've seen a strange thing. I was camped in the farthest garden along the river. The sun went down and the flying foxes rose from the trees in the swamp, and a great bird came and scattered them. He was a hornbill, but he was bigger than the hut in the garden. I was afraid, and I ran through the trees to the river. But there was a crocodile by the canoe, bigger than the canoe. He stood his ground on the bank and opened his jaws and his red throat was as big as the door of a house. And I ran back through the trees, but a snake dropped in my path. He was as long as the rooftree of the House Tamboran, and my legs were stems of grass, and I could not run.

"But the snake spoke to me. He said, 'Follow me,' and it seemed that I wasn't afraid any more when I heard his voice. I followed him and we went a long way.

"We came to a place where he went down into a hole in the earth and I followed him there. It was a long way to the bottom of the hole, and when we got there he looked about him, and he picked up—this."

Kudgil lifted the bright red bangle from the table, and all the eyes swung with his hand. All the men looked at him, and an old man said, "Ee-yah," and his eyes became excited with the hope that flowed into them. Gerlap leaned forward with the rest, and only Laseki was disapproving.

Kudgil said: "The snake picked up the bangle with his mouth

and passed it to me. He said, 'Take it. It is yours. It is from your ancestors who were living and now they are not. But they have not forgotten you. They would give you this, and it is yours.' "

There was talk, a murmuring of talk, and Kudgil waited. He did not hear the talk except as a muttering of voices, and when he went on he spoke very quietly and all the men listened.

He said, "I looked at the bangle as I went on my way. It was a long time that I walked, but it seemed a little. When I came to the water again the crocodile still sat by the canoe, and he didn't slither back into the river as I came near. But I was afraid no longer. I had no fear at all.

"And the crocodile said, 'Come,' and he swung his tail around. I sat on his back and I put the bangle on my arm, and he swam into the river and down under the water. But I could still breathe, and I could see a little. At the bottom of the river the crocodile waited, and I got down off his back. And among the things he had there he looked around, and he found this can of meat."

Kudgil lifted the can, and the eyes followed his hand again. The old man swayed forward in his place, and his eyes were very bright indeed.

"The crocodile said, 'It is yours. It is a gift from your father and your father's father from their plenty.' And I took the can and came again to the riverbank without feeling the water, and the cloth of my lap-lap was dry. And at the clearing the hornbill waited. He sat on the roof of the hut and waited for me."

Now there was a hornbill carved on each of the great peaks of the House Tamboran, and struggling beneath each hornbill a mass of figures, men and a woman. There were hornbill heads carved on the canoes, and on the paddle-heads above the grip; and the hornbill sat over the life of the tribe. In the days before cloth lap-laps, the men wore hornbill heads for a decoration, and they did not eat the bird.

So, when Kudgil talked of the hornbill the men drew in their breaths; and some said, "Ee-yah," very long-drawn at the backs of their throats.

"I sat behind the wings of the hornbill," Kudgil was saying, "and he flew very far and very fast just above the tops of the timber. And the flying foxes scattered before him. We came to a long valley and at the head of it a mountain, stretching into the clouds. On the face of the mountain, on the peak of the cliff was a tree, and the hornbill flew up and into his nest in the tree. And I could see nothing but the cloud and the trunk of the tree reaching down.

"The hornbill took this glass from the nest and gave it to me. And he said, 'Your ancestors sent it to you, because they wish you well.' "

Now there was a movement among the men. They waited, but they were not passive. There was something else in the truth that Kungil had seen, something that meant more than all that he had said, but he could not think of it. He was faint, though he would not show it. Abruptly he put the glass with the can and the red bangle, and sat down in the front of the circle, facing the table like the rest.

Laseki, the headman, was at the table. He wore the bone ring of his authority on his head. His lap-lap was caught up with the leather belt of a police boy and, as did not happen often, the sergeant's stripes he had earned in his years in the service were fastened to the armlet that encircled his biceps.

Laseki had in his hand four straws, and in the quiet he threw one on the table. It looked a big thing lying on the smooth top; as though the women that were the carved legs of the table held it, and it alone. It looked more than a straw.

"There is the glass," said Laseki, as he threw down the straw. "And it seems no more and no less a glass than it was when Kudgil brought it in his pack from the mines at Bulolo. And there is the bangle and the meat. . . ." And he threw down two more straws.

"Such a bangle and such meat is for anyone who has the marks to give Chu Lim, the Chinaman. For there is a big stock of these things in his store; as you have seen. And this is the talk. . . ." And he threw down the last straw.

"For it is in my mind," he said, "that this is a bad talk, and it should come to an end quickly lest more should come of it."

Tombarap, the luluai, came quickly to the table and took up the straws. He was the chief over all, and his power came from the wives in his house. He was a big man, and he had been a power in the days when men were strong. Even the Government recognized his power and called him "luluai," though they had set Laseki, in a way, to watch him; and usually he took Laseki's advice. Tombarap took up three straws in one hand and one in the other.

"These three talks are one talk," he said.

He slipped two of the three straws in his belt and there was a murmur of approval. He set the straw remaining on the table.

"Now Laseki speaks the truth. Yet it seems to me also the truth lies with Kudgil. For we can see as far as the Chinaman, and behind the Chinaman the white men, and the ships, and the canoes that fly. But behind these we cannot see, and to me it is that Kudgil spoke the truth. These, then, are from the ancestors."

He swept the straw to the floor, and carried the glass, the can and the bangle to the other table by the sago-frond wall. Then he came back. He dropped the single straw from his other hand to the table.

"The talk goes on," he said.

The talk went on through the day and into the night. It was Tombarap who made the last decision. "It is a little thing to ask," he said. "We will ask our fathers and they will send us the goods of the white man."

The rest of the truth jogged Kudgil, the matter he had forgotten, and he spoke quickly. "There is more than asking," he said. "For when the hornbill spoke to me of the glass, he said, 'A little thing to carry in your hand.' If I had been ready for more I think he would have given me more. And I have been thinking that the white men, when they await cargo, build a shed they call a Customs shed; and in this shed there is an agent. I spoke of this to the hornbill in the tree on the mountain and he told me: 'You are the agent. Yet you have no house to hold the goods.' So we come now to the building of a shed."

All the men were avid now, except Laseki, who sat in the shadow. They were imagining the wealth of the white man. They had seen it. And very obviously most of what they had seen could come from nowhere but another world. They could see the need of a Customs shed and an agent, and so it was decided. In the morning they set about the building of a shed.

At the district office, a hundred miles downriver, the A.D.O. was breaking in a new patrol officer when Laseki arrived. His arrival was announced by a fat police boy in a navy-blue lap-lap and scarlet cummerbund, heavy with leather, and hot under the blue flannel jacket he wouldn't have parted with for a fortune.

"Blue" Chisholm, the A.D.O., went out to see Laseki; and he didn't return for an hour.

Robins, the patrol officer, looked up from a magazine as Chisholm came in.

"What is it?" he asked.

"Trouble," said Chisholm briefly. "We go upriver tomorrow. Three and a half bloody days against the current. We'll leave at dawn." He filled his pipe, looked up and grinned. "It'll be good experience for you," he added.

"A killing?" asked Robins. He was very new.

"Worse," Chisholm said. "It's Cargo Cult. It'll mean months of trouble." He frowned. "It's new upriver. Don't know where they got it from."

"What's Cargo Cult?"

"A form of envy, I suppose. They build an airstrip and wait for the white man's cargo to come to them. When it doesn't come they make sacrifices to their ancestors or their gods and ask for it. Put on a big feast. Then they kill all the pigs, chop down the coco palms, burn the houses, dig up the gardens. Then we step in and save it going any further, as a rule. And then we have to supply them with rations till they get their gardens going again."

On the boat, when there was little to do but watch the greasy, gray water slipping past, he elaborated a bit more.

"They ask the gods to send them cargo, and when it doesn't come they think they can put up a better argument if they have nothing left of their own. They think their ancestors cannot leave them in the lurch if they have nothing."

"You said, 'Worse than a killing,' " Robins said.

"More trouble. And there's this about it. They think we get our cargo from the next world—can't tell them any different once they get that idea. So they think we interfere with them just to keep the trade to ourselves. They think if they get the stuff, we'll have to live off the bush and they'll be the wealthy ones. So they'll do anything to keep their arrangements secret from the white man—even to killing a white man who might come around. They haven't done it yet, but it's in the cards."

On the second night upriver the garamuts spoke. A drum throbbed as the sun went down—a small message, repeated twice; a tiny sound to carry over the hills. Chisholm, not usually particular about these matters, set a strong guard of police boys to watch as they lay at anchor. He didn't say anything about the drums, and after dinner he suggested a game of Double Patience on the foredeck.

The mosquitoes were getting fierce, and he kept two of the boat boys busy with spray-guns, a third watching the ice, the water jug and the rum bottle. He played a very good game, as the game goes, and turned in some time about midnight.

The next day it was noon when they came round the bend below the village.

Chisholm was using his field glasses at the rail up by the bow. The palm trees about the village were still standing. The huts were as usual. There was a little smoke of cooking fires; and a crowd of people above the landing stage.

"Looks normal," Robins ventured. Then he saw the straggling structures in the water near the bank. "What's all that piling?"

"Wharves," Chisholm said. "For cargo. When it comes."

He stood up and ran his fingers through his thick yellow-red hair, then turned and went down to the cabin.

He came back with a revolver, a .38 Webley. He broke it right down and then reloaded it. Then he cleared his right-hand trouser pocket of a bunch of keys and a handkerchief and slipped the revolver into it.

"You think you'll need it?" Robins asked.

Chisholm pursed his lips. "There are no women in that crowd," he said. Robins looked again. They were near now, and he didn't need the glasses. Men were everywhere, and now he noticed that every man was armed. Most had bows and arrows; some had spears or bush knives.

He looked back at the deck behind him. All eight police boys were there. Two had Owen guns, and they were backed up on the main deck by four boys with rifles. The other two boys with rifles were climbing to the short-deck; and Robins noted with some relief that one was Oragi, who could always be trusted to bring down a pigeon or a hornbill with his first shot.

The boat boys were going about their work as though nothing were out of the ordinary. They disregarded the crazy wharves that had been erected, and warped the craft in directly to the riverbank, making fast to trees.

It was usual for such an arrival to be assisted by a happy crowd of natives. But these villagers stood well back, waiting, a solid semi-circle of men shoulder to shoulder, and backed by more men.

Chisholm said, "It's bad. I want no shots fired unless I am killed. If I'm killed, you'll have to clean this up before you leave. Oragi will help. He knows all about it."

He sat on the rail and swung his legs over. He said, "I won't be killed," and grinned. Robins, moved by what relic of chivalry he could not name, thrust out his hand, but Chisholm ignored it. He dropped to the bank and said over his shoulder, without looking round, "I hope."

At that moment there was a high, full chant raised, like a song, an invocation; and the ranks of the brown men opened at a point a little from one end of the semicircle where a path led from the landing place.

Tombarap, the luluai, stood there in war paint, a spear in his hand, calling to the white man words that meant nothing to Robins. Like the others, today he wore no lap-lap; only the tusks of pigs for a chest ornament, and tasseled daggers in his armlets.

Chisholm walked forward three steps to a place of level ground and stood, and Tombarap came forward, dancing to his chant, self-hypnotized in fury, and shaking his spear. There was a chanting behind him too, now, that grew faster and faster. Tombarap became an automaton, moved by the chant. He danced faster and faster, advancing faster, dancing and plunging his spear now till his muscles snapped like ropes on a bucking colt.

There was no doubt but death was in his mind. He was Death; Death in a brown skin. He had one purpose and it was one with him and it was Death. He came at Chisholm, and Chisholm just stood.

Then Chisholm's hand was in his pocket, and he drew the Webley. Robins saw his thumb slide quite slowly with the safety-catch, and when Tombarap was twelve yards away Chisholm fired, and a tiny hole appeared on Tombarap's chest, in the center, between the nipples that had been ringed about with keloid markings until they stood out like mountains from a desert. But Tombarap didn't fall. He came on. He came on silently, but he came, dancing and stabbing, and his spear arm never faltered.

To Robins' amazement Chisholm returned the Webley to his trouser pocket. It was vivid, the way Robins saw it. He saw Chisholm's thumb slide back with the safety-catch and the revolver drop in the pocket and Chisholm take his hand away again and wait. And yet at the same time Robins could see Tombarap come on without faltering.

Well, a man may see much in six seconds. And when Tombarap came within striking distance of his target he spun and fell backward with his head to Chisholm's feet, and his spear pointing back along the path he had come. Tombarap was quite dead.

And all the men had seen this that Robins had seen, and the riot, if there had been a riot, was over. For if they looked for an omen, they found it in the manner of the luluai's death.

There was a talk; and Chisholm gave the badge of the luluai to Laseki, the headman. Afterward he walked about the village, Laseki with him, and saw the new hut, almost half as big as the House Tamboran; and he asked the meaning of the hut. Laseki told him it was a Customs shed for cargo.

Chisholm had Kudgil brought to him and Kudgil had certain fears.

Chisholm said, "Here is a Customs shed for cargo and there is no cargo. But there are times the Government has need of such a house. You own this house?"

Kudgil said, "Yes."

There was more talk, about Kudgil and about Bulolo; but nothing of the visions Kudgil had seen. At the end of the talk Chisholm appointed him headman beneath Laseki, and gave him Laseki's old bone ring of authority.

He explained to Robins afterward: "Apparently this was the Joe who started all the trouble. He's found out how to use people now —not many natives do. So we might as well use him. There's no one else for headman, and Laseki will keep him in order—Laseki's a good man; served in the police force sixteen years.

"And now let's get to hell out of it and let them have their funeral. The gardens are gone, but they still have the coconuts. The pigs are gone, but there's plenty of game. We got them in time. It was something of a classic, and you were lucky to see it work that way."

Robins said, "Why didn't you give the luluai a second bullet?"

"Nothing. No reason. But I speak only once, and my gun speaks only once. A matter of pride. It goes a long way with these people."

Kudgil had taken the ring with a face impassive. He thanked Chisholm at some length, but there was a question in his mind. He knew that, before he saw the truth of the matter of cargo and brought it to his people, he could have attained to no authority.

Perhaps the white man had a reason for making him headman and the reason was connected with the cargo. There was a reason for everything. The truth he had seen in that hut in the garden was still very clear to him. The cargo had not arrived, to be sure; but perhaps the time would come. Perhaps at some future time he would talk again. In the meantime he would remain the keeper of the Customs shed, and wait.

When evening came, Kudgil sat in the doorway of the Customs shed by himself. Piligat, the old man, the hunter, saw him there and came stealthily, carrying something wrapped in his lap-lap. He laid it down before Kudgil. It was a gold-lip pearl shell, half cut, but not in any way impaired.

"It is a small thing," Piligat said. "It is something I give you because I have held you a friend for a long time. It is a gift." He hesitated uneasily, and Kudgil said nothing.

"It's in my mind," Piligat said, "that the wharves and the Customs shed no longer have a use. Yet it seems to me that if a thing is there, a use will be found for it. And it is true that such a thing as a bright red bangle does not grow in the bush."

Kudgil looked at him and stood up and found the bangle, and brought it to Piligat and gave it to him. And this was an answer to the gift of the shell; because a man who brings a gift requires a gift in exchange.

Piligat said, "It is true also that for such a shell as I have given you, Chu Lim, the Chinaman, would give me twenty such bangles. But it seems to me that with wharves and Customs sheds someday there will be many bangles. And I will be glad, because in that day I will still be your friend."

This Kudgil understood fully. When Piligat had gone, Kepa came with three shells of the green sea snail. Before Tupai could arrive— he saw Tupai on the platform of his hut—Kudgil went to Gerlap, the father of Talua. He sat there in front of the old man for twenty minutes and talked of nothing, while Talua shrank into the shadows of the hut. But he saw that she looked at him and that she smiled briefly before she looked away.

"There was talk of a bride-price," he said suddenly, and Gerlap nodded. He had been waiting for this.

Gerlap said, "These times will be hard. There are no pigs and no dogs. There is sago but nothing in the garden. In hard times the bride-price would be less."

"It is a good price," said Kudgil, and Gerlap's eyes widened. "Tomorrow I bring the price."

Talua stood up and walked past the two men and down the steps into the village street, and on toward the bush. But before she went she looked at Kudgil again and his heart leaped up.

"It is a good price and a good bargain," he said again.

Gerlap gave him his hand, and it seemed there should have been a lot to talk about with his prospective father-in-law, but he was impatient, and he was gone very soon. He found Talua waiting at the rim of the bush; and all his dreams came true.

The Head-hunters of Ianagl

PATROL OFFICER Ron Harrison, twenty-six, tall, fair, unmarried, not overly ambitious and normally a little lazy, was in the third and last week of a routine river patrol when they brought him news of the murder of the women. He was encamped for the evening in the village of Mubaidia, a small and impoverished community of sago-eaters, thin and miserable people who enriched a diet composed mainly of starch with small additions of grubs and snake meat. Harrison, in country new to him, with a team of ten strange constables under a corporal whom he did not altogether trust, was in that hour looking forward to a speedy return to his pleasant, if fairly primitive, headquarters at Arodi.

It was the corporal, Nundi, who now brought him the news of the killings. Nundi looked and acted like a paragon among men, thereby engendering that distrust which Harrison tried neither to explain nor to abandon. He was a well-built native, well groomed according to police regulations, with shining belt and harness and scrupulously clean body, trimmed hair. His skin was shining with health, his eyes were bright, and his only self-indulgences were occasional cigarettes and an irritating tendency to hold himself superior to other natives, particularly to those not connected with the service.

He was completely unperturbed now as he came to Harrison in the tent set up on the dancing-space in front of the fighting platform of the long house in Mubaidia village.

"Sir," he said, "there has been a killing in the village of Kerabini three days up the river. There is a man who has just now reached Mubaidia by canoe, and he tells of the killings."

"Killings?" Harrison said, sitting up. "What kind of killings?"

"Just killings for the taking of heads, sir," Nundi answered. "Not a killing of vendetta. A killing of women. Nine women of the village of Kerabini."

"Where is the man?" asked Harrison.

"I'll get him, sir," Nundi said. "But he can talk only the place-talk of Kerabini."

"Get him," Harrison said impatiently. "And get an interpreter."

"I can interpret the talk, sir," Nundi said. "I speak it well enough," he added a little smugly.

"You're too goddam' good to be true," Harrison said, but he waited until the corporal was well away from the tent, and he said it under his breath. Then he stood up and followed the corporal into the open air.

The informant was a bush Kanaka, rather better-formed than the sago-eaters of Mubaidia, but only an average specimen of riverman; and his wild eyes were big with fright. As soon as he saw Harrison he launched, without being told, into a frantic tumble of words.

"He says that forty men of the Ianagl in three canoes came and took the heads," said Corporal Nundi.

"What was the way of it?" Harrison asked. "Let him begin at the beginning and tell whatever he knows. Was it a raiding party?"

Nundi conducted question and answer with the man for fully five minutes until Harrison was thoroughly annoyed. Nundi paid no attention to him at all, but continued questioning the man, and though he was tempted to break in with questions, Harrison realized the interruption could serve no useful purpose, and indeed would lower his prestige in the eyes of the people, now gathered round, only partly comprehending. Nevertheless the uninformed waiting was an irritant, and he wished he had confined his request to simple questions and answers.

Nundi finally turned to him and said:

"It was not a raiding party, sir. The women were working in the garden in the afternoon of the day before yesterday. The gardens are close upon the riverbank, and there is only a fine screen of bushes and trees, growing here and there. There were nine women and a young girl in the garden, and the girl was lying asleep at the edge of the garden under the trees. The nine women were weeding, with their heads down, and they were watching their work and did not see the river, though it was so close to the garden. And three canoes of the Ianagl men came down the river and they saw that the women did not observe them at all, and they drifted with the current down past the garden until it was out of their sight.

"Then they came ashore and surrounded the garden. They crept round the garden very quietly and when they were stationed all about it they ran and came quickly and rushed on the women and struck them down and cut off their heads."

"Was the village watching, that all this was known?" asked Harrison skeptically.

"No, sir," said Nundi, with complete candor and gravity. "The village is a little way from the garden. It was the girl lying asleep under the trees. She woke as a man ran past her, not seeing her. She saw the men run and take the women quickly unaware, and then she ran for the village. And when the people of Kerabini village came to the riverbank the men of Ianagl were already in the three canoes. They jeered at the men of Kerabini. And besides, not more than twelve of the Kerabini men were then in the village."

"Did they know the names of the Ianagl people?" Harrison asked.

"The headman, Timu, was the leader in one of the canoes and the leader of the party," Nundi said without hesitation and without checking with the Kerabini man. "And others were Mangalun, Gaupa, Bapi, Masin, Tareno, Yawin and Autitip. And there are others of whom the names are known in Kerabini. Ianagl is a growing village, sir, with nearly seventy fighting men. It is not a well-protected village, but they have no strong neighbors. There are not more than thirty women in Kerabini now, sir, and they have lost nine. The leader of Ianagl, this man Timu, is well known all up and down the river. I know this river well, sir, and they fear the man Timu. I think that he swaggers more than he kills, but he has a bad reputation."

"Dammit, his reputation doesn't come into this," Harrison almost snarled. "And leave your thoughts out of it."

Corporal Nundi looked surprised. He had given an excellent report and he knew it, as did Harrison.

"Well, sir, they said this Timu was the leader in this taking of heads. I said it was not a raid. I think they found by accident that the women were unprotected and so they struck. That is my opinion, sir."

Harrison brought pencil and paper out of the tent and made long and careful notes of the evidence of the man from Kerabini, and in the morning they turned their backs on his headquarters at Arodi and went on up the river.

At Kerabini he checked the evidence, and, subject to only a slight conflict of identification, entered the names of thirty-four accused among the notes he carried. He camped at the village and in the morning set out, leaving his carriers behind and taking only his armed policemen, for the village of Ianagl.

. It was to be his first contact with these people, though he had read of them in previous patrol reports as "a sullen and unco-operative tribe." According to these earlier patrol officers they made no attempt to trade their native foods, to assist in pitching camp, or to offer as carriers. They kept themselves to themselves, standing with folded arms which were never empty of stone ax or steel trade knife. They were ax-fighters, who used the bow and arrows but not by preference. They were suspected of cannibalism, and there was always considerable doubt whether the round house with cooking stones in the village was ever used for the baking of pork, although the stones seemed always freshly black and greasy. There was always a doubt, too, whether the human shinbones and armbones with which their spears were tipped had come to them legally through the deaths of tribes people. Not all the skulls in skull-racks belong to victims of the people; not all the bones used for implements are the bones of enemies. Nevertheless the Ianagl were ugly customers, and according to their infrequent contacts, patently so.

They were ugly in appearance, too, flat-nosed, heavy-browed, and possessed of certain facial characteristics which, some said, pointed to Malayan strains in their ancestry. In spite of these they were big men; light in the leg but with the heavy arms of the canoe people. Harrison's first glimpse of them was surprising.

In the broad and deep canoes they used on the river, he had been able to set up for himself a kind of half-hammock of net; a type of deck chair in which he took his ease on his river journey-ings, for when a man is committed to wary inaction for periods of weeks, he comes out of it best whose inaction is comfortable. It is best of all if he can sleep for longer or shorter periods. Harri-son wasn't sleeping, but he had a book of Emerson's essays which he carried with him for the simple reason that it would last him a long time. He read a paragraph or two and then thought about it, fitting it into a game of hazard he played with the long-dead philosopher on the proposition that Time had outwitted him and proved him wrong. It was a good bet—Time had made a monkey out of Emerson on a majority of his theories, and his assertions.

Sitting there, reading and thinking and sleepy in the sun, Harrison was aroused by a shout of "Sail-O" from the policemen. He looked up and saw, fortunately at a distance of several hundred yards, two heavy canoes coming round the bend of the river above him.

His force was at this time divided, with five rifles in his own canoe and five in the other, under Corporal Nundi. The other canoe was under the trees by the bank, while his own was in midstream as the boys crossed to take advantage of the diminishing current in the shelter of the other side.

To his amazement, as soon as they came in sight, the canoes upriver put pace to their paddles and swept down on his own craft at considerable speed. There were fifteen or sixteen men in each canoe. They were painted and bedizened with feathers. They had yellow circles about their eyes and red bands of paint on their cheeks, and they wore headbands of cowrie shells sewn into tapa cloth. They shouted and yelled as they came down the current, and the overriding emotion of Harrison, who had encountered and set ambushes, but never before had to repulse natives in direct attack, was one of amazement. Just as he decided that the warriors were committed to the attack, the police boy Watsiup, sitting behind him, pulled at his arm and spoke low and earnestly, keeping his eyes on the advancing canoes.

"Sir," he said, "the fashion of these people is not to fire arrows in a fight between canoes. They do not fight with spears. But they will drive their canoes alongside ours and overset them, and when our men are in the water, then they will club them with the stone axes, and none shall get to the bank."

"Well, thanks, Watsiup. That's very nice to know," Harrison said humorously. Then he realized, with a concentration which was admirable but misguided, that the leading canoe coming to the attack had completely overlooked the presence of Nundi's canoe by the right bank.

He called out in a loud voice, but as though he were addressing his own crew. He said, "One volley, Nundi, over their heads. All together when they are opposite you."

And almost immediately upon his words the rifles spoke.

The effect was fantastic. It was comic opera. In the narrow valley, overshadowed by cliffs, the sound of the volley was magnified beyond reason. For the men in the leading Ianagl canoe it came from nowhere. They fell in all directions, though they were unharmed, some leaping from their stance in the canoe. These overbalanced, and threw the remainder in the water. All swam immediately for the bank, keeping their heads below the surface. They vanished in the bush and Harrison saw them no more that day.

But in the after canoe, fifty yards behind the first, there was no panic. It swept in to the attack with no reduction in speed. Harrison leaned forward, wondering how he was going to deal with this, and he heard the voice of Nundi.

"Aim true," the corporal yelled. "Aim true, and fire."

Three figures at the paddles of the attack canoe fell, and again the canoe overbalanced, and the men went into the water; only this time the water was stained with blood. Again the swimmers reached the bank and vanished immediately into the forest, but three bodies bobbed on down the current.

Harrison watched them go. They represented the first deaths for which he had ever been personally responsible. His men pulled their two canoes into the bank and disembarked. As Harrison stood up he realized he was still carrying the book of Emerson's essays in his hand, and he put it down quickly.

He was flushed and angry, and the book overbalanced the scale. "You dolt," he yelled. "You fool. You spawn of a crocodile." All the tendons of his limbs were taut and quivering. He walked up to Nundi, and for a second it hung in the balance whether he would commit the unforgivable sin of striking him with the flat of his hand. He put his hands on his hips instead.

"Who gives the orders round here?" he asked.

Nundi looked down. "I thought there was not time," he answered.

"You thought! You thought! I'll have the stripes off you," Harrison raged. But already the realization was overtaking him that he was making a fool of himself.

"The Government does not kill unnecessarily," he went on in a quieter voice. "We do not take lives. We save these men even if they are murderers, and bring them to the court alive. Only if the court says, 'Die,' will they die at the right time, in a proper manner. I told you to fire in the air."

"I have done wrong," Nundi said. He raised his eyes and looked at Harrison, and then went on stoutly, with more confidence than Harrison had seen a native display. "Truly you told me to fire in the air, and for the first volley I did this. But the second volley I fired without an instruction, and it seemed it would be wasted if it, too, were fired in the air. There was no surprise in the second volley. The man in the lead of the second canoe was Tumi, who is the headman of Ianagl village, and of whom we have spoken."

Now Harrison was caught. The second volley had been rightly placed into the canoe, and he knew it. He had spoken from the access and the release of tension; perhaps because of his embarrassment at finding the volume of Emerson still in his hand; and unfairly, because of a personal dislike of the corporal. But, still unfairly, he disliked more than ever the opportunity Nundi had given him to change the subject when he had talked about the headman. Nundi was too smooth a character, he felt.

"Don't forget," he said. "This is the last warning. Don't take it on yourself to give orders. Or to act without them either."

"I am sorry, sir," Nundi said honestly. "If I had thought at the time it was wrong I would not have done it. I will do what you say. I will not make any more orders." He hesitated. "I hoped the Government would soon make me a sergeant," he added.

"Follow orders, or you will be a police boy again with no stripes at all," Harrison said.

There was blood on a trail through the undercarpet of the jungle, and Harrison would have followed it except that the war party had been so completely routed. He decided that a quick approach to the village itself might bring him there in advance of the warriors on foot, so they embarked and paddled swiftly upriver. In half an hour they arrived at the village, but it was deserted.

Ianagl consisted of one long house set in a clearing at the hollow of a bend in the river, so that the large fighting platform, set out in front of the high horned building like a raised terrace, commanded two river reaches, a long straight stretch upstream, and a shorter one downstream. At the back of the fighting platform a door, three feet high and narrow enough for one person only, gave entrance to the house itself. Through such a door, the Ianagl could be very selective indeed about their visitors. Inside it, a short but high-vaulted hall was furnished with a rack of human skulls, each set in a separate pigeonhole in the rack. There was a clay fireplace in the center of the hall, and there were small carved tables standing about, mats and pieces of pottery by the walls.

Down the side of this front hall a passageway led to a number of small cubicles which filled the remainder of the long house. All were empty, but all showed signs of recent habitation. The house itself was raised above the ground, perhaps ten feet up, and in front there was a clear space for dancing. There were canoes drawn up on the bank near the front of the house, but these, when examined, proved to be in disrepair.

In the clearing behind the long house, there was a round house, a roomy building in which were fire stones and the ashes of a fire. Against one wall there was a pile of bones. Most of them were human, from arms and legs, and they were obviously stored for later use in the preparation of weapons. There were no broken bones in the heap.

There were also three or four smaller houses in the clearing, for the boys of the village, and for women with babies so young that their crying might disturb the elders in the night. From the back of the clearing, paths led into the forest in all directions.

The police boys scattered to search the village, and from them came a cry that brought Harrison out of the long house. But it was only an old woman, worn and careless, with wrinkled shanks and gapped mouth. They could get no sense from her.

While the police boys were together, Harrison spoke to them, outlining his plans.

"First we return to the village of Kerabini," he said, "for it will be a long trail; yet we should not leave it to get cold. So we will get the carriers and the other canoes, and interpreters and guides from the Kerabini. Then we will follow the Ianagl men until we hunt them down. Now our stores are gone, and we cannot spend too long on the hunt, but if we can get some of the men who took the heads, then we will take them to a court and later come back for the others. If we can get the headman, Tumi, we can put a halt to the taking of heads for a time, and we can come up the river again for the others."

This was the program they followed, but at Kerabini they ran into unexpected delays. The small village, already short of labor because of the death of the women, was hardly prepared to supply extra carriers and interpreters for the expedition; and their food supply was small. Moreover, when the men were persuaded to join the party they were frightened. Several times Harrison considered that the wiser step might have been to return to Arodi with his party and set out afresh.

In addition he had advice from the Kerabini that the Ianagl people would undoubtedly have taken to the sago swamps several miles above the village, and Harrison shuddered at the thought of combing the sago for men like these, searching for a track, and following the track through water sometimes waist-deep in single file among the heavy, vicious growth; following it into ambush as likely as not, or, with fortune completely on his side, perhaps coming unexpectedly on his quarry, one or two at a time, in isolated huts in the dark gloom of the swamp.

He stayed at Kerabini two days, and on the third morning decided to put in a concentrated effort for ten days and then return to base. He felt extremely helpless in that wild and alien country.

Something of his indecision and uncertainty transmitted itself to the boys, and it was a quiet group of five canoes that moved upriver. The remaining Kerabini people watched them go, quite silent and apparently unmoved. As they came upon the bend of the river that would, when traversed, disclose the village of Ianagl, Harrison saw Nundi lean forward and speak to his paddlers, and his canoe drew forward of the others, approaching the bend on the inner side, as was wise, for the current ran less swiftly there. For no reason at all, Harrison was about to shout to Nundi to tell him to get back with the others, when he saw the corporal hold up his hand, and his men stop paddling, and the canoe drift quickly back downriver. With a few strokes the paddlers put the craft alongside Harrison's.

"We are lucky," said Nundi. "The people of Ianagl are back in their village."

Harrison was astounded because the possibility hadn't occurred to him. Instantly he blamed himself for not taking it into consideration and noted glumly that Nundi obviously had.

"If the paddlers and the interpreters and the carriers all get into three of the canoes, then perhaps we can come up close on the village before they see us," Nundi said.

"That's pretty obvious," Harrison commented. Then he corrected himself. "Yes, we'll do that."

They ran the canoes ashore at a mudbank at the side of the river, and while the men attended to the transfer, emptying the two lightest canoes which would be used for the attack, and placing the gear in the others, Harrison called Nundi and the other police, and, squatting in the mud, drew with a stick the plan of the village and the river.

"Your canoe will go first, Nundi," Harrison said, "for even after they sight the canoes, I will be more noticeable than you. After we come in sight of the village, make all the speed you can, and bring your canoe ashore on the upriver side of the long house. I will land downriver, and then we will run together behind the long house so that we may cut the house off from the bush behind. You saw the men in the village, Nundi?"

"They walked about, here and there," said Nundi. "They are doing what they do every day, and the men sitting on the fighting platform are talking amongst themselves."

His eyes were bright, and he was looking forward to the attack with pleasure, Harrison thought. And he thought also that the actual joining of arms would show him what kind of a man this corporal was, whether he was all brag and surface, or whether he was a steady man in a fight. Only in battle may a man show those qualities for which other men admire him, for in peace they are an embarrassment.

"When they see the canoes, the men walking about the village will run to the long house for their weapons," Harrison said. "They will not run away without their weapons. If we get behind the long house we will have them trapped."

The plan, direct and simple, went even better than he could have hoped. The canoes had rounded the bend and were well up on the reach to the village before the lookouts on the fighting platform sighted them. For an instant all was confusion. There was a high falsetto calling from the platform, broken and interrupted by staccato shouts, and the clearing was filled with running men, all converging on the long house.

The police canoes drove ashore to either side of the long house, perhaps three chains apart, and the policemen abandoned them running, just as the arrows began to fly from the long house. The two lines of police ran together in a V, like a flight of ducks. The arrows thickened about them and, though no one was hurt, Harrison yelled, "Under the house. Get under the house." The files moved in under the long house, and there was time to consider their position.

Not much time. There was still movement at the back of the village. A young woman ran from the trees, snatched up a toddling, naked baby, and disappeared again. Two old heads peeped comically from a hut doorway, perhaps steadied by the thought that they could not be seen. And as the men paused in the shelter of the great building, perched ten feet high on its piles, arrows came, more accurately than the first, from the surrounding bush. His troops were steady, Harrison noted, handling their bayoneted rifles like veterans.

Beneath the house was a small canoe, and some sago troughs carved from logs were stored on a small platform built between four of the piles. Harrison pointed to them.

"Three men, pull them down. Take cover and wait here," he said. "Follow me, the rest."

He raced to the front of the building and up the broad steps, saplings lashed horizontally at a slope, onto the fighting platform, now deserted.

Ahead of him was the doorway, tiny, dark, menacing. It was built so that a man must stoop low enough to be helpless on his entrance. It made a man's head assume the position exactly propitious for hitting with a stone ax. Beyond the doorway, Harrison knew, was a murderer with a stone ax. But surprise had carried him this far, and he counted on surprise to aid him yet. He dived at the doorway, yelling, "Follow close." And just as he bent his head to enter the door a weight hit him on the hip, and, taken off balance, he reeled and crashed over the side of the fighting platform to the ground.

Weird thoughts come to men at times like these. He was most acutely conscious of the fact that, although he had his revolver in his hand and it was cocked, with his finger on the trigger, it had not gone off with the fall. Then he was racing round and up the steps again, and he remembered, or became aware, or puzzled out what had hit him. It had been Nundi's hip.

Two police boys were still struggling to get in that narrow door. He pushed them aside and went in. Corporal Nundi lay on his face on the dark floor with a great gash in the center of his head. Seven village men were lined up, their weapons on the floor, and the police boy Watsiup had his bayoneted rifle making a considerable depression in the unbroken belly-skin of the man Timu.

Lance-Corporal Kevi was on his knees beside Nundi, and Harrison, seeing the fighting situation well in hand, dropped down beside him.

"Is he dead?" he asked.

"He lives," said Kevi.

The line-up of the Ianagl men produced eight. Another was hiding, in sweating terror, in one of the compartments of the long house. Beneath the house, emerging from their barrier of sago troughs, the three policemen had caught one more; but ten or a dozen others, breaking through the thatched walls, had gained the bush.

Harrison got his ten prisoners handcuffed, got into the canoes, and raced back for Kerabini. He and his policemen contributed shirts, and made an improvised bed for Corporal Nundi, and Harrison himself tended the wound. It was a bad one. The ax had hit across the front of the skull and bitten into the bone. Harrison had seen worse injuries, but here death had been close.

Watsiup was talking.

"When the ax struck Nundi, Lance-Corporal Kevi took Timu by the arm," he said. "Kevi ran through and held Timu who held the ax, and threw him down. Then we were all through the door."

The canoes were alive with the buzz of conversation. There was shouting and talking and a lot of boasting. Harrison smiled to himself. Already the carriers who had been on the mudbank throughout the fight were relating details as though they had been present, and the constables were correcting and adding to their stories. Harrison listened, down on his knees cleaning Nundi's wound, carefully shaving the hair from the skin over the skull, working with a solution of Condy's in the river water.

Nundi opened his eyes and watched him, and then he struggled to sit up.

"Lie still," Harrison said.

"I am all right, sir," Nundi replied.

He lay for awhile with his eyes open, apparently untroubled by Harrison's operations on his wound.

"Again I broke orders, sir," he said. "There is something in me that makes me. I hope I do not lose my stripes, sir," he said.

This caught Harrison unprepared, and Nundi was talking again before he could answer.

"I was too quick for him. He was not ready," Nundi boasted.

"You were too quick for me, too," said Harrison. "Lie still. And don't talk."

"Sir, I must tell you. I was sorry to push you over. I thought it had to be done. Truly a leader should be in the lead, but we couldn't spare you well, sir."

"Still the smooth character," Harrison thought. "He's consistent." But there was admiration in his appraisal. Aloud he said, "Where did you learn to use your hip?"

"I am a footballer, sir," Nundi answered, and tried a grin. "A good forward, sir."

"A good man." Harrison nodded. He leaned forward. "A good leader, Sergeant Nundi." The corporal looked up at him.

"True, sir? *Sergeant* Nundi?"

Harrison nodded. "I think so, Nundi. I'll write a report tomorrow. When you are better it will be Sergeant Nundi. But you will have to follow orders."

Nundi closed his eyes. In spite of his wound and his pain he looked happy.

Sergeant Pangae,
Detective

SERGEANT PANGAE squatted on the ground, inspecting his rugged features in a large trade mirror, switching his head from one side to the other to find the best effect, and pulling his mouth into twisted shapes as he did so. He was wearing a once-white lap-lap, stained but clean, a gleaming white athletic singlet, and an old and battered Stetson, twined round and round with a length of the climbing antigonon, its bright pink flowers contrasting curiously with the stained gray hat and the teak-dark face beneath it. Apparently satisfied, he returned the mirror to the large and bulging canvas bag that hung by his hip from a length of shoulder webbing, stood up, straightened his shoulders and marched across the lawn, up the steps, along the wide veranda and into the office of Ramage, the District Officer. Here he came to an impeccable halt, threw a Guards salute, as befitted a prominent member of the New Guinea police force, and reported:

"Sergeant Pangae, plain-clothes, waiting for orders, sir," he said.

A shirt-sleeved Ramage, sitting precisely behind a tidy desk, looked up. There was the ghost of a smile behind his eyes—Sergeant Pangae on plain-clothes duty was as predictable as Sergeant Pangae in uniform—same lap-lap always, same athletic singlet, same old battered felt hat wreathed, it always seemed, with the same pink flowers. But he was the best man Ramage had on the station, and this was a special job.

"You know this place, Naramai?" he asked.

"Yes, sir," said Pangae. It had been practically a rhetorical question. Pangae was old in the district and knew every place, though Naramai was remote: a small station in a fertile valley deep in the mountains. There was a patrol officer there, presiding over a small post office, savings bank and district office. The Methodist mission had an establishment near by, and a trader named Riley kept a small store and a bakehouse. It was off the beaten track and the natives, though long accustomed to the rudiments of civilization, lived by hunting and by their gardens. They traded a little copra but the major part of their money came from the wages brought home by the young men who sometimes worked a year or two on the plantations near Rabaul, or the mines at Bulolo.

The district office at Naramai also served the contiguous villages, Kumbilip and Kwaragi and Lauolo, and half a dozen more in the valley, each removed from the others by a mile or two of forest track.

"I've had a letter from Mr. Goodland, the missionary," Ramage said. "He is worried because the savings of the people are disappearing. They don't have much money to spend, but a lot of what there was has vanished. They've taken a good deal of money from the bank, and they haven't spent it at the mission or the trade store. I don't know whether we can do anything about it." He picked up the missionary's letter and read it again.

"There's about six hundred pounds, at least, not accounted for, Mr. Goodland says. That's a lot for that district. Well, there's no harm in them taking money out of the bank and spending it if they want to, but I'd like to know where it is going. I want you to find out, Pangae."

"Yes, sir," said Sergeant Pangae.

"There's just a chance that some flash boy is getting money from the others on some excuse or other. If so, you can make an arrest. There may not be anything like that at all. Mr. Goodland may be making a mistake. All I want you to do is find out if they are spending money, and what on.

"Now the patrol officer, Mr. Curledge, tells me the withdrawals from the bank have been fairly heavy since he has been there, but they have all been in small amounts, nothing to worry about. But I do know from the remittances I have sent him, that the consumption of money in the district has gone up way above average. Anyway, get up there and find out. Take a month—six weeks if you need it—it'll take you four days to get there. But get back as soon as you can."

"Yes, sir," said Pangae. He saluted again and walked out, the pink antigonon flowers nodding and dancing on the decrepit old hat.

In four days he was in the Naramai district, and his disguise preserved his anonymity for exactly five minutes. He was at the junction of the track just beyond Kwaragi where it forks to go to Naramai in the east and Kumbilip in the northeast, when a once-familiar voice hailed him.

"Where do you go, old enemy?" it said. "What brings you here to Kwaragi?"

Pangae stopped and considered, waiting while the man walked up to him. He was not greatly disturbed at the penetration of his disguise. Its main value in his eyes was that it put him on a par with police of an advanced category in other lands; but he did not particularly want to meet Kasimus of Kumbilip. In the big war, Kasimus had been an enemy indeed. He worked for Japan—in fact he held high non-commissioned rank in the Kempe Tai—and Pangae

vividly remembered his own last assignment, which was to seek out
Kasimus in the Jap camp at Yessan on the Sepik and shoot him at
the first opportunity. Pangae was at that time newly returned from
another important foray, a reconnaissance he made, singlehanded,
of the Japanese installations near the mouth of the river, a foray in
which his presence had been discovered in the first day or two.
Nevertheless he had stayed close in to the camp for ten days until
his information was complete, and this in spite of a constant search
that was made for him; and with rifle, bayonet and knife he had
taken seventeen Japanese lives (souveniring one of the heads for
old times' sake) and the lives of three of the natives attached to the
Japanese armies.

So soon as he had reported back he had been sent on to Yessan,
whither he walked, and when it was safe, canoed, for six weeks,
arriving there to find that the camp was occupied by Allied officers,
and the war was over. As a matter of form he had, nevertheless,
tried to shoot Kasimus, taking careful aim from a stance in the
center street of the mile-long crowded village; and he was indignant
when he was disarmed. That was when they had given him the medal
for his previous reconnaissance, a British Empire Medal which,
when it was awarded to one of the native police, was given for very
conspicuous bravery indeed.

As a result of this encounter there remained a peculiar relationship
between Pangae and Kasimus. They were not friends; they were no
longer enemies; and each had a respect for the other based on the
knowledge that each had been a key figure in the fighting armies of
the opposed countries. Pangae had no particular wish to spend much
of his time with Kasimus.

Nevertheless, any contact would be useful, he knew; and he also
had a suspicion, based on prejudice, that if there happened to be
any roguery rampant in the district Kasimus was as likely as anyone
else to be at the bottom of it. Therefore, when Kasimus approached,

he answered the greeting in a way that put himself and his time at the other's disposal.

"I'm going walkabout, Kasimus," he said. "Limlimbur"—which means: "I'm free as the air, having a holiday and doing what I feel like doing."

"Will you come to Kumbilip, then?" asked Kasimus.

"I might as well. Later I will go to Naramai."

"You are still a policeman? Do you still like the work?"

"I am still with the police. But I am getting old, and sometimes I long to go home to my village," Pangae said untruthfully.

"We all grow old," said Kasimus. They walked along the forest paths together, through the dappled light, talking, as men talk, of little things of little moment, just livening the day.

Kumbilip was a mountain village, set out against the sky on a spur of the ridge, occupying a subsidiary height. The trees were nearly all cleared away from the ridge so that there would be no cover for an attacking enemy; though in Kumbilip there had been no fear of enemies for forty years past.

The houses, about fifty of them, were clustered close against a road that split the village in two, and in the center of this road was a flat space for dancing, and here the village celebrated. Here the old men sat at night, sharing their betel nut and their tobacco and their conversation. And here they clustered round Pangae on his arrival, talking and listening and forming their judgments.

Pangae talked a great deal, as was polite for the stranger, the newsbringer, but he talked nothing of importance to himself for the first three nights. During the days he made friends, sitting about the huts, once or twice going hunting with the men, or visiting the gardens with them while they cleared the ground, or helping to kill a pig. He looked for new wealth—for an abundance of steel or cloth or ornaments; but he could see little that had not obviously been in the village for many months. Some new money had been spent. Not even as much, however, as in many poorer places.

He was waiting for the right time to lead the conversation to certain topics, and on the fourth evening his chance came, for a youth named Didsira had been to Naramai and come back with news.

"There is to be a landing field for aircraft in Naramai," he said. "All the people are to work one day each week and build an airfield."

Kasimus nodded.

"That was sure to come," he said. "And someday there will be a road with cars and trucks; and someday after that we will live in houses built of sawn timber."

There was a general murmur of disbelief, spurring Kasimus on.

"No, this is true," he said. "Someday the village will have cars of its own, and trucks to do the carrying. When I worked for Japan I learned to drive a car. And a big boat on the river. I tended the engines and drove the boat; and these things are simple. We all can learn."

But Pangae shook his head.

"I, too, can drive a car, and I can drive a boat with an engine, and not the big engine only, but the little engine that is clamped to a dinghy, and goes put-put-put," he said. "But I have been to the white man's cities. I have been to Sydney; and I have been to London, and that is a city bigger than Sydney. And the things that lie behind the cities are not simple things like driving of cars. I have seen things bigger than Kasimus dreams about; and perhaps they will come here someday, but then living will not be simple any more."

"What things?" asked Didsira.

Pangae took a cigarette from the fingers of Kasimus and puffed on it a little while before he answered. He leaned back and considered for a little while. And then he said:

"I have seen a whole village that ran on wheels through the country, a village with houses made of iron. And each house had thirty or forty people within, and there were twenty houses tied together, and in front an engine, bigger than any engine you have ever seen. And when people wanted to go from one place to another they went into the houses and sat there, just as you sit within an aircraft only with more room. And they ate when they were hungry and slept when they were tired, and left the village when it came to the place they wanted to go; so they came without walking, and without carrying of burdens.

"And more than this: for the village that they call a train, when it came to the city, went in a hole under the ground; and beneath the hole was another hole, and every little while one of these trains ran through, sometimes one over the other, for there were so many people going from one place to another."

There was silence for a little while, and an old man asked him: "How did you see this, Pangae? And when?"

"I went to London for the crowning of the Queen, I and the best of other policemen," Pangae said. "London is a cold place, and raining. It is no good. But it is full of such marvels, and more people live there than there are trees in the bush. Sydney is cold also, though not so cold as London. And these are only a few of the things I saw. I saw men take iron, and make such an engine as pulls the train. I saw it from the beginning to the end; and they did nothing that I could not have done myself, with a little learning; just as I have learned to drive a car. Yet I could not have lived my life in their fashion.

"There was no one man who did anything that I could not do— or you, Kasimus, or Didsira, or any other man. And I saw that with machines a little man could lift a mighty engine high in the air, and turn it round, and put it on its road. And this, too, I could do. It was a little thing to learn, like driving a car."

"When the cars come to Naramai I will drive again," said Kasimus. Pangae took no heed.

"These were not the marvels of the city. These were marvels but not the great marvels. I saw a bridge so long and so big that one end would set down at Naramai and the other at Kumbilip. I saw a House Tamboran four times as high as the highest of high trees. They called it a cathedral, not a church. I saw a house full of tobacco"—Pangae looked about him "—longer than this street, and higher than this street is long, and as wide again." There was open disbelief on the faces now. "It was a house full of tobacco, and the tobacco was packed tight, and machines in the roof lifted the bales to the top of the pile."

"This is something to think about," said Kasimus, but Pangae shook his head.

"No," he said. "For these were the things that I thought about: the people, in numbers greater than you can imagine, and packed together like the pebbles in the stream, yet all of one kind. And all shouted with one voice when they saw the Queen. There were men of all colors, from all the world over, men of worth and men of little worth, but they were all of a kind when the Queen rode by. I tell you I was myself one of them; there were yellow men, and tall black men from Africa, and white men; I was one of them, and when the Queen passed by I did not feel the rain on my face or the cold striking at my bones. And here was power.

"But there were these things, too, I thought about: that there were shops in Sydney and in London selling flowers; and people all day going to shops and buying flowers, and paying more than a month's wages for a few flowers they could carry in their hands."

"Then I would sell flowers," Kasimus laughed.

"Then if I wanted a flower to put in my hair I would have to pay you money. Then I would not put a flower in my hair," said Pangae. "The truth is that there, in those places, so many people live so close together there is no room for flowers. And the village is so big there is no time to walk; and if a man would spend a little time with a friend, he must go to him in a car or a train; and he must pay money to do it, and for that he must work harder.

"There is a man to grow the flowers and a man to catch the fish, and a man to grow the fruit; and if you take a little fruit from his tree the police will take you."

"Nevertheless, we here are to have an airfield, and someday we will have a road," said Kasimus. "And I will have a car to drive."

It was here that Pangae saw his chance.

"Then you will think you know everything," he said rudely. "But the driving of a car is the last of many things, and it would be better if you were to learn the first of them. It would be better for us all," he added.

"What things?" asked Kasimus.

"Many things. For behind every man in a car in London is a man in a house of paper. A man who reads and writes and keeps a tally. And this is the man who has the power. For reading and writing and the making of figures are the tools of Government. And when the Government becomes strong and the roads come, and houses of wood and stone, then the man who reads and writes will be more than the man who drives a car. When the people are so many they are like the fish in the sea, the making of reports and their reading is at the root of the Government's power. It is like a magic."

"Yet we governed ourselves without this reading in the old days," said Kasimus.

"Without reading you can govern men who cannot read, but not the men who can," Pangae said. "A man with learning is like a good hunter who follows a trail and reads the signs correctly—he will catch up in the end, and make his kill."

"Yet Master Curledge, who is the Government at Naramai reads and writes and spends much time at it; and we can deceive him. Only one man in four works on the paths on the days appointed;

and we otherwise have learned to have our own way," Kasimus bragged.

"There are good men and there are others in the Government," Pangae said. "There are good men and bad everywhere. And the white man is not better because he is white, but simply because he has learned more—and not of the driving of cars, either. In Sydney there are men who work on the roads, who dig holes and carry burdens; and I think all of them drive cars. But there are no men of our color there to do the work. Work is everywhere. And everywhere there must be a man above work, who will direct. For us, here in this our country, it must be a white man because we do not know enough. This is what I have learned: that learning is power, and I have not learned enough."

"I do not see it," Kasimus demurred. "Power is wealth, and motor cars, and big boats. These things do not come by learning."

"Learning is different in our world. It is knowing the world—the forests and the hills. But in the world that is coming, it is knowing other people. So learning is power. I will try to show you in a little way, for I have a little learning. Give me the bankbook you hold from the Government office. I will tell you your business, whether you are a man of substance. Now show me the book, and see."

"I have plenty of money," Kasimus said. He got up from the circle and walked to his house and brought back the passbook from the savings bank. Pangae opened it, poring over the pages.

"You are a wealthy man, Kasimus. You have seventy pounds."

"So much?" exclaimed Kasimus. He was pleased. Two or three others left the fire and went to their huts.

"You went the week before last and put money in the bank. You put three pounds there. You see I know your business. It is better to learn this little book than to learn a car. The book comes first and then the car; and the white man's world is both together."

"This may be true," said Kasimus. "Nevertheless, I put eight pounds, not three."

Pangae examined the book again. "I cannot read very well," he admitted. "Nevertheless, for the little I can, this book tells me certain things."

Didsira was at his side, holding out his book.

"Tell me how much money I have left," he said.

Pangae angled the book to the firelight.

"There are seven pounds left in the bank. Ten days ago you took some money out."

"Two pounds," said Didsira. Pangae looked at the book again.

"That may be. Two pounds," he said.

"I thought I had more pounds than seven," Didsira complained.

There was a little flurry of business while some of the villagers brought their books to Pangae and learned the state of their balances. He was not surprised to find that none of them already knew. But he called Didsira back.

"This two pounds," he said. "You are not long back from the mines and have little need of money. Were the two pounds for yourself?"

Didsira shook his head. "For the father of my father," he explained.

"But the father of your father is dead."

"Even so, he had need of it."

"Tell me," Pangae asked, "how do you speak with the father of your father?"

Kasimus cleared his throat.

"It is a thing that happens to me," he interrupted. "Sometimes in the night I go and talk with the spirits. I can do it when I want. Sometimes the spirits talk with me. While I am away in the land of the spirits sometimes they come to my empty house and talk with the people. This is the way it happens."

Pangae leaned forward. "It can happen whenever you want it to?" he asked. He had been impressed that, of all the bankbooks he had seen, only that of Kasimus showed recent deposits. The remainder all showed withdrawals.

Kasimus nodded.

"I talk to the spirits whenever I want."

"This I would like to see," said Pangae.

The talk fell into normal channels and withered away with the fire. But Pangae reviewed his decision to go to Naramai on the following day and instead spent a little while longer in Kumbilip.

"I would like to talk with my father," he said to Kasimus next day. "It is many years since he was eaten by the crocodiles in the Yaisima swamp. I would like to hear how things go with him."

"There will be a present for me," said Kasimus promptly. "A present of money—a pound. It puts me in danger to go to the land of the spirits."

"That's only right," agreed Pangae. He handed over a crumpled note.

"The night after tomorrow I will go to see the spirits. If your father comes in my stead you will talk with him."

"If my father comes there will be another present," Pangae promised.

Kasimus looked pleased.

"There is merit in other things than reading," he remarked.

The night of the séance was dark and still, and a little crowd of men, forewarned, gathered in front of the door of the hut where Kasimus lived alone. The women of the village were in their own huts; the children were long asleep, and the gathering was silent with the heavy alert solemnity of people who wait for a miracle. A nightjar was making his rhythmic detonating call somewhere back in the trees, and the night rustlings of small creatures seemed pre-ternaturally loud, as though a thunderstorm were building up.

Kasimus, by the steps of the hut, spoke softly to Pangae.

"I will sit by my bed and wait for the spirits to take me. But let no one come in the hut or something evil might take them. This is for me alone. I know my way back from the land of spirits. In a little while this coconut I put at my door will fall to the ground—I will kick it as I go, but you will not see me. Then the hut will be empty, as you may see. But do not stop long inside, or the spirit of your father will be angry if he does not find an empty hut."

He went inside, and pulled a plaited leaf into place so that it concealed the doorway.

The intensity of the silence grew. The people sat like carved figures, the firelight outlining the curves of their backs as they squatted on the ground and glinting from the corners of their eyes. There was a rustling movement within the hut; and then, in a little while the coconut at the doorway rolled to the ground. There was a murmured acknowledgement from the men squatting near the hut.

Pangae climbed the steps and looked inside. It was dark there, but the embers of a dying fire threw a little light and he could see the place was empty. There were the water carriers stacked in a rack beside the door, the palm-trunk bed upraised from the floor and an army blanket thrown on it. There were pots near the fire, and a dance-mask on the wall picked up the last fragments of light, and glowed evilly white. The dark eye-spaces above the great hooked nose seemed filled; they seemed to possess the power of sight and be fastened upon Pangae; but he touched the mask and it was loose upon the wall. He swept his hand through the space above the hut veranda, a little space where in some huts people slept, and in others stored their goods. The space was empty. He went outside and rejoined the people squatting on the ground. They had all collected at the side, rather than at the front of the hut, and sat silent, looking expectantly at the grass-thatched wall.

After awhile, it might have been ten minutes or quarter of an hour, a voice spoke from within the house.

"Pangae," it said. "Pangae, my son. Is it my son?"

It was not, apparently, the voice of Kasimus, but it was too low, too soft, to be positively identified. It might even have been the voice of Biba, who was Pangae's father, and whose name might not now be mentioned.

"I am Pangae," the sergeant replied.

"You would like to talk with me?"

Pangae hesitated, looking round at the men of Kumbilip. They were staring, all of them, at the blank grass wall from which the voice emerged, taking no notice of him. The night was very silent.

"Only to know how you fared," said Pangae. "To tell you that all things go well with me; and to know how you fared."

The voice, so low as to be almost indistinguishable, told him of the spirit land. His father, it seemed, still had much pain of the bite of the crocodile that had ended his days; he still had the heavy legs afflicted by elephantiasis that had carried him on earth. And sometimes by reason of the fact that he could not work very well, he was hungry. He was in a good land, but he could not make the best of it, because he could not work so well.

"I need money, my son. Can you give me a little money?" asked the voice.

"I have money," Pangae said readily. "But how do I know you are my father?"

"Is not the voice the voice of your father?"

"The voice is the voice of my father truly," Pangae said. "But I cannot give money to a voice. A voice has no hands."

"Roll up the money in a little ball, and throw it in the hut. How much money can you give me, Pangae? A pound?"

"I have three pounds. But if I throw the money in the hut how will I know it comes to you and not to Kasimus? For Kasimus owns the hut, and he will find it."

The voice was silent.

"If you are my father, put out your hand for the money," said Pangae. "For this is not a thing that Kasimus would do, and it will be a surety for me."

The silence continued a little while. The squatting audience straightened, a man here and there. Here and there a man looked fearfully at Pangae, who thus conjured the spirit into a visual presence. There was a rustling of the thatch, and then the fingers of a hand, moving slowly, protruded a scant few inches.

"Where is your hand? I do not see it," Pangae said. The other watchers, silent as the mountain peaks, now turned to him again in amazement; but the hand, palm upward, extended farther through the thatch. Pangae looked in his shoulder bag, appeared to extract something, and came forward to the hand. Suddenly he gripped it, pulled hard, and brought an arm, up to the shoulder, through the thatch. At that moment there was a sudden sharp cry from the hut.

"Truly the voice was the voice of my father, but the hand is the hand of Kasimus," Pangae said. He brought the hand down by the foundation pile of the house, and beckoned to Didsira. "You, man," he said. "Tie this hand to this pole, while we find the rest of Kasimus."

There was a silence inside the hut. When the wrist was lashed tight to the pole they went inside.

There was a false wall, leaving a space perhaps eighteen inches wide at the side of the hut. Pangae pulled away the grass and disclosed a discomfited Kasimus. The only other apparatus was a light rod leading from the hiding place to the door, so that the coconut could be toppled. As with all good money-making plans, the perfection of this one had lain in its simplicity.

After a crowding hustle of jeering villagers had inspected Kasimus, Pangae squatted down beside him.

"You know I am a policeman, Kasimus," he said. "Now I arrest you. And tomorrow you travel with me back to headquarters; and I think you will go to the calaboose."

He went outside, released the sorceror's wrist, and went to bed in the village long house, secure in the knowledge of a good job done.

In the morning he selected Didsira and two other villagers who had paid spirit money before, to go with him as witnesses, and they set out. But when they came to the fork of the roads, he took the one that led to Naramai.

"You will need money," he said, "but this money the Government will repay. Nevertheless, I am not a rich man, and we will be some days on the road; therefore, take each one two pounds from the bank."

"I, too?" asked Kasimus.

"You, too," said Pangae. "You also eat."

He squatted down a little way from the district office. There was little point in his reporting to the patrol officer; and he had no intention of making explanations. And when the other four came back he took their money and their bankbooks and put everything in his shoulder bag. There were protests, but he quieted them.

"You are all witnesses that each took his money from the bank, and that I took it all. It is safe. Master Ramage will see you get it back. It is a police matter. Something you would not understand." He looked a little triumphantly at Kasimus.

Four days later he marched them into the police barracks and made them wait while, in his house, he removed the old gray felt with its renewed wreath of pink antigonon, the athletic singlet and the stained lap-lap, bathed himself carefully, and dressed in the navy-blue uniform of the police. They waited longer while he polished his leather accouterments, and when he was fully satisfied with his appearance he marched them to the district office, leaving them on the veranda while he reported to Ramage.

"Old friends meet," commented Ramage when, after he had heard the story, he wandered out to look at the prisoner and the three witnesses lined up on the veranda. He knew Kasimus of old.

"A very good job, sergeant. We've found out where the money was going anyway. And Mr. Goodland will be satisfied."

"Sir, there is a little more to report," said Pangae. Ramage looked at him questioningly and led the way into the office, out of earshot of the prisoners. There he produced the four bankbooks and the eight pound notes from his shirt.

"This man Kasimus is a little thief, I think," he said. "Obtaining money under false pretenses. This other one—I don't know what to call it." He opened the first bankbook. It belonged to Kasimus. "When I saw the book first time it said that Kasimus had put three pounds in the bank. But Kasimus said he had put eight. Didsira said he had taken two pounds out. His bankbook said four. Now when we came away each man took two pounds out of the bank, and there were three witnesses for each man to say he did it. But the bankbooks say different." He showed the entries—there were three withdrawals of four pounds recorded, and one—in the book belonging to Kasimus which had the biggest balance—of five.

"Good Lord!" said Ramage. He sat down at the desk and examined the books.

"You are sure of this, Pangae?" he asked, and answered himself, "Yes, of course you are."

Pangae nodded. "I am sure, sir."

"Curledge! That's a bit unhappy. That's a bit of a problem," Ramage said, talking to himself.

"You could have arrested him yourself, Pangae," he said, but the sergeant shook his head.

"A little time does not matter," he said. "There will be another white man to take the place of Master Curledge, and it will be better if the people do not know why. The Government is for people to look up to. Let another man be the Government at Naramai; then he can arrest Master Curledge."

"Talks like a book, that fellow," Ramage said to the cadet patrol officer in the outer room when Pangae had gone. He stood at the window and watched him march down the road. A few yards from the district office he stopped and plucked something out of the hedge —a long, heavily-flowered spray of pink antigonon.

"But he's the best detective in the force," Ramage added. He leaned over and wagged a finger in the youngster's face.

"Don't ever underestimate a native," he said. "It's poor policy. I'm sending you up to Naramai in the morning to arrest a man who does, and bring him in—Curledge."

"Just for that?" asked the cadet patrol officer, surprised.

Ramage nodded. "Just for that," he said with some finality.

The Exiles

*T*HE *theory of colonizing by the method of the tache d'huile is not new—the Romans used it; and for all we know colonizers thousands of generations before the Romans. As an oil stain spreads in all directions from the point of application, the emollient influences of civilization spread slowly but inevitably from the edges of the selected site of first contact. In New Guinea such influences were applied at certain chosen centers and then an interwoven series of cross-patrols from center to center hastened their distribution. The establishment of the centers evoked a heroic contribution from the individual— there is no lesser term applicable.*

Mount Rentoul is one of the highest peaks in New Guinea; the Rentoul River is a considerable stream; Alex Rentoul, in whose honor they were named, leads a quiet life in retirement in a Sydney suburb, though his heart inhabits the beautiful bays and forests of these tropic islands. He is a small, inconspicuous man, rosy cheeked, white haired, and suffering somewhat prematurely from the infirmities of age. But he is remembered in New Guinea for a stalwart, almost a pedantic, honesty, for an indomitable courage, and incredible devotion to duty.

He was a young man with a good war record when, in 1923, the swamp-dwellers of the Turama River, an unprepossessing crowd of sago-eaters who obtained their proteins from wood grubs, swamp

195

*turtles and the meat of their fellow men, forced themselves upon the
attention of the Administration. Two tribes of them, the Umadai
and the Wariadai, combined to decimate a smaller tribe for the
purpose of using their heads in the ceremonial of baptism for a
fleet of new canoes; but there was a survivor of the raid, a girl little
more than a child, who gave the names of men among the murderers to the Government.*

*Rentoul was sent to clean up the area. A Resident Magistrate,
he was accompanied by a young patrol officer, H. L. Johnston,
nineteen armed constables and twenty-five carriers; and with this
pygmy army his instructions were to establish a police camp with
permanent buildings, to patrol thoroughly all the villages of the
Umadai and the Wariadai and those of another tribe, the Doriomo,
thus bringing under complete and peaceful control all the villages
of the lower Turama River, and to arrest, within a period of one
month, seventy murderers believed to be implicated in the raid.
The country where he was to operate was sago swamp, in which he
often had to travel waist-deep in mud; the natural dangers, ranging
from crocodiles to disease, seemed all enormously magnified here,
and the people were the most viciously intractable yet encountered
in New Guinea. But Rentoul was to achieve the practically impossible, a little later than planned.*

*He and Johnston were both stricken by fever and after a com-
paratively short period he sent the patrol officer back to civilization,
where he died. Rentoul went on and established his camp, shedding
no native blood, though his own police, forbidden to return fire,
were several times wounded by spears and arrows. He waded day
after day through swamps to his waist, racked with fever; he established that the number of murderers did not much exceed forty, and
he arrested thirty-four, later making firm friends with most of them.
He explored the entire area in a period of four months of incessant
rain; and he did it so well that never since that time has it been*

necessary to make more than routine patrols throughout the district.

At the end, he staggered out of the swamps, nearly five months after he had entered, to a surprise meeting with the Lieutenant Governor. To his own amazement he was unable to speak. He stayed silent for twenty minutes.

"I felt such a fool," he says today. "H.E. [His Excellency, the usual reference to the then Administrator Sir Hubert Murray] was being so nice to me, and I couldn't talk. It was silly of me."

He had made one mistake, and through the mistake felt himself responsible for the only loss of lives of men under his charge in the whole of his career. He had delegated responsibility at one point to the wrong man, Kari, an Umudai interpreter who claimed close friendship with the Wariadai. This Kari was sent off, at one stage, with five canoemen to establish a contact. The following morning his canoe came back down the river, with one man aboard, paddling frantically to report the failure of the enterprise.

Rentoul hastened to the village and found the headless bodies of the four missing men. In time he arrested these new murderers too, and it would take a book to do justice to the epic. The records are lost, destroyed needlessly by the Australian Army in wartime; and they live today only in the uncertain memory of an aging hero who, in any case, thought his actions no more than his duty. He takes pride, however, in the fact that three times in his life he stood on the top of a high mountain and looked around him, and each time knew himself to be the first civilized man to look on whatever his eyes could see.

Rentoul is chosen to appear here almost at random. He was only one of a good company who tackled impossible tasks cheerfully, looked after the health and the welfare of their men in enemy country, fought as men fight, without hatred or discernible emotion, and regretted the necessity for their little wars. He loved the people under his control, and his love was reciprocated. But the men of *this company, magnificent in their achievements, were isolated in their strength, bollards of control in an amazing sea of drifting humanity.*

First to the new country had come the men running from the law and also the opportunists like the one who, in the year before the establishment of Government, bought four square miles of the best land adjacent to the best harbor, Port Moresby, for "one axe, one adze, three tomahawks, three sheath-knives, one grass-knife, twelve looking-glasses, one bundle of hoopiron in small pieces, six long pipes, twelve short pipes, one piece of Turkey red cloth, one piece trade handkerchiefs, five pounds of tobacco and one gimlet."

There were men like John Guise, heir to one of the greatest names in France, who lived out his life in a beachcomber's shanty and there so conducted himself that his removal became one of the earliest concerns of the first Governor, although it was never effected. There were men like Nicholas Minister of whom his wife (dead only these last two years) reported that, having on board his schooner a native who had displeased him, he had sunk a big fishhook into his shoulder, cast him overboard on the end of the line, and towed him astern until he drowned. There were anti-social outcasts, and there were men whom adventure called and the lure of gold and pearls, and some few attracted by the challenge of writing their names in the history of the Pacific. There were even men brought, as they were also brought to Australia, by the lure of hunting the trickiest game in the world—homo sapiens—with powder and shot; and some of these were not above paying for their trophies—well-tattooed heads—buying them from more primitive hunters who used the bow and arrow, the bone dagger and the rattan noose.

There were the dealers in mother-of-pearl and tortoise-shell, the hunters of birds of paradise, the men who knew how to turn discoveries of plants to fortune, the men who looked to re-establish family fortunes upon the virgin soil of a new country. This ragged army was presently joined by an influx of gold miners; by the disbanded escort of the first Governor; by runaway seamen and runagate soldiers and the whole apostasy of civil order.

But also came the leavening. Even at their worst these communities had some sense of proportion. In the first hotels, for instance, the reckoning was based each morning on the number of empty bottles flung from the windows on the previous evening, and the score divided equally among everyone known to have visited the establishment. Once the representatives of Government were added to the communities, disorder was on the wane. The missionary had already established himself in the land and his numbers were increased. The respectable woman made her first appearance, greatly to the expressed distaste of the established community, who saw in it, and rightly, the end of the era. Came the doctor and the judge and the banker; and the storekeeper replaced his red-sashed pajamas with a suit of tropical white.

The swashbuckling outlaw went to earth, his lair concealed by the fresh and vigorous growth of respectability; and the protests, while raucous, were not sustained, for, except in a few spectacular instances, the pickings for the lawless had, in that community, been poor.

The adventurer continued to come to New Guinea; but there was no place in the world beyond the reach of the law; and the outlaw did not congregate. The communities were too small for him.

In the first fifty years of Administration the quality of migration changed. The new arrivals still included a high proportion of the anti-social and the temporarily anti-social—young men whose sweethearts had jilted them, who had failed their examinations, been disbarred, or thrown out of the medical profession for illegal practices. Or at least the proportion might be considered high by comparison with analyses of other populations. To some extent this is still the case, as may be indicated by the fact that New Guinea has rather *too many suicides and crimes of violence for its population. There were also men who arrived blameless, but found the temptations of New Guinea too great. Some missionaries left the church to seize inviting business opportunities; some were requested to leave because of their uncontrolled personal idiosyncracies.*

The Administration, convinced that the white population should provide an example for the indigenes, partially solved this problem by the deportation of undesirables, and today also it exerts a limp control over the new arrivals. And in the development of the centers of population, the more solid citizens formed a stable core round which communities have developed in a manner not too far removed from the norm.

But there are no centers for the education of adolescent white children. They are sent off to school in Australia, and a majority settle there. And there is no real necessity for the white man or woman to engage in physical labor. A plenitude of servants does the work and encourages an unhealthy selfishness which has too wide a play.

Until the war came to the Pacific these factors were conditioned by the responsibility which lay upon members of the community in regard to the indigenes. Particularly was this so for the District Officer or Resident Magistrate on a remote station. He carried out the duties of policeman, prosecutor, judge, banker, postmaster, doctor, dentist, jailer, engineer, surveyor, architect and any other specialist of whom his community stood in need. Sometimes he went a great deal further.

And when he was faced, as he often was, with communal calamity—mass murder, or threatened rebellion, or epidemic—he took the situation in hand, solved the problems in the best way he could see, and then sat down to write a report on his activities. They would receive judgment perhaps two months later. And many a man, in making the wrong decision, wrecked his career.

Today the pressure is less. Faced with a problem, the District Officer radios headquarters for instruction, and accepts no personal responsibility. Perhaps it is a better system, but I think not. For it leaves the solution to any problem in the hands of a man sitting in an office, hundreds of miles removed from the upset. And it certainly does not breed the kind of man reliable in an emergency who was run-of-the-mill under the old Administration. There are good men in the service yet, and many of them, but they are hampered in their activities by red tape and office control, their responsibilities have been lightened, and modern transport laughs at the distance between them and their fellows.

A patrol which, in the early days, could have been carried out only with the aid of perhaps sixty carriers, of whom a high proportion were carrying their own food and who needed, of course, additional protection by native police, is now rationed from the air with helicopters. It is cheaper, more efficient, and the patrolling officer's risks and responsibilities are minimized. No one would want to revert to the earlier methods. But those methods produced the men who wrote a glorious page in New Guinea history.

The completely modern officer is also more out of touch with his natives.

In older days a man, administering a post efficiently, might have been left there for years. He could speak the local language, and knew his people and understood them. I could instance one "Doc" Bellamy, who singlehanded, over a decade or more, transformed the peasantry of the ten thousand people under his control, into a kind of stalwart yeomanry. The value of the result was open to some question, but the achievement was undoubted. He made them owners of property—pigs and coconut palms; and it was property existing where there had been nothing before. He supervised, at practically no cost, the planting of something like 120,000 palms, adding this to his other duties. The old-time officer, like Bellamy and Rentoul and dozens of others, including some who have achieved fame, was revered almost as a demigod, and his word was law. His example led the men under his command to great heights. Very frequently, in a skirmish, the men themselves delegated to one of their number the sole responsibility for watching for the safety of their officer, and this was shouldered frequently at the expense of the guardian's life.

Today's officer stays seldom more than two years in a station, and then as often as not is shifted to a place where a different language is spoken. The natives are quite oblivious to his personality, for he is merely one of a long chain of representatives who have assumed power over them at bewildering intervals. Increasingly civilized, they have become increasingly litigious, and a great deal of his time is taken up with their domestic issues. Unless he is very conscientious, he is prone to attend to these—the stealing of a pig, the defection of a wife—at the expense of larger problems, which he leaves for his successor by the simple process of not reporting them. His predecessors of twenty years could not afford to do this. Apart from others, the considerations of personal safety alone intervened.

His predecessor also had to throw himself fully into work—alternatively rum-addiction—to escape the effects of ennui, not being surrounded by others of his kind. A strict discipline was the only means he had of keeping intact the quality of his mental powers. And a strict discipline was demanded by his superiors, particularly the Administrators of the period who made frequent visits of inspection to all the outstations. Today there are too many outstations, too many staff members to occupy his attention in the major centers, and the current Administrator has seldom seen some of the stations in his charge.

But of long habit, the outer habiliments of discipline are maintained. A squad of armed police mounts guard night and morning on the raising and lowering of the flag, even when the officer is in temporary quarters on patrol, and is the sole representative of his race. Gardens are tended, lawns cut, the rudest of official habitations cleaned from end to end daily. If there are not enough prisoners to perform the menial tasks, the average officer can soon find an excuse to fill the local calaboose with another lot. He arrests a squad for not performing their weekly day's stint on the local road and the station is manned once more.

The Government officer's relations with the missionaries and the traders have frequently been difficult. In older days when a poll tax was imposed on the natives, missionaries frequently came under fire for collecting donations a step ahead of the Government man collecting tax. If the native was going to lose anyway, he felt he would just as soon give to the first applicant; and the average missionary was never too self-effacing with his collecting-box. Missionaries are apt to use, too, a great deal of unpaid labor. I have seen schoolgirls attending a mission which was Government-subsidized on condition that it taught lessons to its students for twenty hours a week. And I have seen week after week in which the girls spent ninety per cent of their learning time in weeding the mission vegetable garden. The standard of teaching is low and the responsibility of imparting instruction not seriously shouldered. And finally the missionary tends to think of himself as a lawgiver; and instances are frequent in which he has assumed some of the prerogatives of Government.

There are missionaries in all the denominations whom I greatly honor and respect, but I must admit to a personal distaste for the one who hastens to wash after shaking hands with any of his flock, for another who in discussion concedes that the indigenes are "little more than intelligent animals," and for the many who use individuals in their care for their own profit, and, too often, for their own pleasure.

Like the missionaries, the traders and plantation owners come in good and bad grades, but here the standard, if it is on the move at all, seems to be lifting slightly. Partly this is due to the tight Government control of labor; but in greater measure it is in deference to the increasing commercial independence of the emancipated native. There is a great deal of room for more improvement; but the natural controls governing ordinary business practice will ensure a greater sense of responsibility in the future. In the past there has been no country in which the customer was so consistently wrong; but today the native himself is venturing cautiously into the commercial world.

This in itself is the greatest symbol of change. There are few heads taken in New Guinea now; although die-hard suspicions were aroused when, recently, a new arrival from New Zealand was permanently lost while hunting deer in the bush a few miles from the thriving capital of Port Moresby; and quite a few unpublished opinions held that the unfortunate was a victim of the ancient urge of head-collecting which may still inflame individuals of the Koiari tribe. If that is true, however, the New Zealander was the unfortunate exception which proves the rule, for most of the natives of that particular area are distinguished by an increasing sophistication.

On the whole, it is obvious that the change is for good. And where white elements of the population have lost status or privilege in the new New Guinea, that loss must be accounted small in evaluation of the total gain for the country. Nevertheless, the European domiciled there bleats unhappily for the years that are past. His desire to return gets vivid illustration in the almost annual discoveries of "a new Shangri-La, a valley of peace, cut off from the world and inhabited by a fortunate race"—which, of course, it would be a crime to disturb.

Fully fifty per cent of these newspaper elysiums are ruled by beautiful white queens, and the people are almost white. Well, it's true enough that many a white man carries a deeper tan than some natives. I remember a girl in the Central Highlands, tall, comparatively beautiful, and jetty black; handsome enough that a millionaire who was visiting insisted on being photographed with her. On a subsequent visit I caught a glimpse of her after she had washed off the pandanus oil and fire-black in one of her infrequent ablutions; and I was amazed at the creamy consistency of her skin color, long protected by this locally esteemed beauty preparation from the sun. Central Highlanders wash seldom. They live on the mountain ridges to escape the fevers of the deep valleys and for protection against neighboring tribes; and the water carried laboriously to the tops of the spurs is much too valuable to waste in washing.

The general pattern of the Shangri-La and its beautiful ruler is of wishful thinking: the desire to return to the days when any improbable discovery could lie along the next mile. If, of course, a queen of Caucasian descent existed, her environment would have made her thought patterns indistinguishable from those of her dark subjects.

It is natural also that the white man would like to return to the days when he ruled as a kind of supernatural emissary among the people; the days when a certain missionary carried to his death the proud title "Saligigi"—The Taker-Out of Teeth; and imposed a considerable power by virtue of the progressive activities of his dentist, back in Australia. Almost everyone tells the story of the planter who kept his natives working by taking out his glass eye when he left the job, and leaving it on a stump in full view of the impressed gang. At least eighty per cent of today's population knew the man personally; they recount the adventure as an indication of the lower intelligence of the black man; and they seldom mention the native in the same modern legend who circumvented the boss by throwing a cloth over the eye. And miracles have been wrought by a little rudimentary knowledge of schoolboy chemistry; but for this the field is more limited in every year.

There will always be those who sigh for the days that have been. And if the dawning tomorrow does not bring the same kind of elementary opportunity as was yesterday's, there will be other, more challenging chances. And it is good to remember that the qualities of courage and resource which distinguished the best pioneers are incapable of suppression. They will be always evident when the occasion calls for them.

Brown Jonathan

THE chair Brick Wynfield loved to occupy stood normally on the corner of his veranda, its design and construction both shrieking its homemade origin. Hammered together from packing cases, it still bore the legend "Nestlé's Condensed Milk" on the back-boards that had been worn smooth with khaki shirt-backs. It was almost a part of Wynfield. Sometimes he sat there when he held a court, dispensing justice with an impartiality and a wisdom that went beyond the book he followed. From it, he had condemned murderers, investigated tribal killings, heard complaints of wife-stealing and mayhem and petty thefts. Here he had sent men to their fate, some to the gallows and some to prison and some happily to their homes. Sometimes, therefore, the chair had given him the thrill of absolute power. Sometimes, too, it had given him happiness, and sometimes, in it, he had sat through periods of misery.

Mostly, as today, it gave him relaxation. It was placed at the corner of the veranda where it caught the morning sun; and the afternoon storm, as regular as the sunrise itself, slanted away from it. And from it, with his feet on the lower of the two rails that guarded the veranda, Wynfield watched daily a scene which, at first sight, never failed to be breathtaking in its beauty.

To the west, the trees on the lip of the valley broke apart and the gap was a frame for a mighty waterfall where the river dropped into a chasm out of sight. Above the fall, the mountains loomed close. The fall itself seemed hardly more than calling distance away, its volume was so mighty; but the slow, tumbling descent of the water and the muted rumble of its power arrested at the foot, betrayed that it lay in the middle distance, half a morning's walk away. To right and left of the gap, the chasm of the valley walls crowded in behind the eucalypts on the brink, only a tennis-court length from the veranda. In the mornings a permanent rainbow gauged the strength of the valley's sunlight above the tumbling water. And between the veranda and the valley lip lay a wealth of flowers; tree-supported most of them, blazing a riot of reds and yellows against the background of green trees and mauve hills. Three kapoks, feathery stylized etchings of trees, interposed a delicate tracery of design between the eye and the water.

This was the front of the house, the front garden, the aspect which, in civilized countries, suburbia turns to the world. But here, the visitors, the occasional pilots of cargo planes from the airfield, the even less frequent missionaries who negotiated the jeep road to this outpost, seeking one favor or another—forever seeking favors—came upon the back of the house, the boys' quarters, the yards and produce gardens, the orchard and the outbuildings and the tended tennis court, before they came upon the house. It was inevitable, because of the great cleft that was the valley, and the way the station lay between it and the airfield. For the whole establishment was pivoted upon the position of the chair on the veranda; and the best show it could muster was for the chair's occupant, who had brought about the establishment's existence.

Sitting in the chair, Sebastian Wynfield—he hated his given name but never rejected it—felt something of the ease of the man who has got the better of his bargain with the world. In his way he was a king. Nineteen thousand people looked to him for guidance and leadership, and most of them would have obeyed his slightest com-

mand. Nor would that command have been given unthinkingly.
Wynfield was their policeman, their judge, their doctor and dentist.
He chose their spiritual advisers. He kept them to their own laws
as well as the laws of the white people, where the systems were
compatible; and he had an understanding of crimes committed
sometimes when they were not. Wynfield was power. He was the
Government and above the chiefs; and the land prospered.

Something of this may have been in his mind on this evening as
he watched the swift clearing of the early night sky. Then, breaking
across the muted roar of the waters which in this place was silence,
came the transgression of discordance, the ugly, upraised voice of a
nagging woman, urgent, malevolent, minor, sounding monotonously
repetitive diminuendos of antagonism.

Wynfield continued to sit where he was, but the little movements,
the play of his fingers on the cloth of his shorts, the awareness of
his eyes, ceased. As he sat, the night closed down and took the
valley and the waterfall into its shade; and shortly his wife came out
on the veranda.

"I'm going to have my bath, Brick," she said, and her voice still
carried the audible elements of her disgruntlement.

"All right, May, I'll come round," he said. He leaned forward
to knock out the dead dottle from his pipe against the outer edge of
the veranda rail. "I still don't know how you get on when I'm not
here."

"Don't care much either, I suppose," she returned tartly. "You
certainly seem anxious enough to get away whenever you find an
excuse. Well, I just have to take the risk when you're not here. I'm
damned if I will when you are."

"I've told you a hundred times there's no risk," he said.

"No risk?" she scoffed. "No risk till it happens. Every white
woman in New Guinea is taking a risk with these black hounds
sniffing round, and you know it."

"Oh, May," he said. "It's a lot of rot."

"Look at the police news," she said. "Seven years in the calaboose for some coon Bebu for entering a white woman's house after nightfall. Rot? What do they make the laws for? I suppose you know better than the people who made them. *They* don't trust the coons, and that's good enough for me."

"Let's get it straight, May," he said. "That boy went into a house at Bulolo, on the goldfields. That's where the laws were made for. And that's not because the natives can't be trusted. It's just because men without women can't be trusted. You have thousands of natives without women at Bulolo, working at the mines. You have thousands more round the big white settlements, hundreds round the plantations. Men without women. In wartime there wasn't an army camp in any civilized country but women were in danger in its neighborhood. Get it into your head. It's men without women you can't trust. Up here, in the mountains here, where the boys all have their own women, there's more safety than there is anywhere else in the world. Now stop making trouble, May. You have no troubles except those you make for yourself."

She wasn't satisfied.

"Just the same," she said. "You've got the same laws here. You'd have to do something pretty quick if one of them laid hands on me."

"I'd hang him," he said. "I'd have to, and I would. But I'm not worrying. The only reason for the law being here is that any of these boys might be off to the plantations at any time, and it's better they know something of the law. And maybe"—he grinned—"to keep visiting women under control. I don't make the laws, but I carry them out, and the boys know it. Anyway, go on and get your bath, and I'll watch the lantern. It's a silly habit you've got into, and I shouldn't do it. With Parimu about the house you're as safe as you would be anywhere. He'd do anything for me."

She put her hands on her hips.

"You're a fool, Brick. You'd trust anyone. That murdering coon is as bad as the worst of them. You want to catch him looking at me from the corners of his eyes, just once. You wouldn't trust him. He's been carrying on with that slant-eyed Eva, too. He's a murderer and a lawbreaker by your own account. But you can trust him. Oh, yes, you can trust him."

"He killed a man, and that was a long time back," Wynfield said. "By the laws of his people he had to kill him. He did time for a year and wiped the slate clean. Since then, he's been just about the best boy a man could have. Parimu? He's a friend of mine. Now, be your age, May, for God's sake, and slip off and have your bath."

May Wynfield's rite of the bath was as elaborate as Cleopatra's. It required darkness and light in the proper proportions. It required water heated to the exact temperature. It required servants and guardians and seclusion, all mixed to an exact recipe.

She had developed the rite shortly after her first experiences at the mountain station where the people, who had never seen a white woman before, assembled in their thousands in the first days of her advent. They plucked at her clothes and peeped down her shirt-front and felt her trouser-legs and crowded in on her, seeking to establish that she was flesh and blood, as they were; that she was cast in a similar, though obviously more heroic, mold. They rubbed her arms to see whether the white color might be a paint of a particularly fine texture. They were very normal in their curiosity and their persistence.

The bathhouse stood a little way from the house near the lip of the valley where the bath water could run away down the hill. It had two rooms, the first, at the entrance, floored with layers of split cane. Here one undressed. The second was the shower proper, and consisted only of a room equipped with a hanging container of water which the bather released into a gentle and rather uneven shower by pulling a cord. The floor was made of whole bamboos with a space between each, so that the water drained rapidly away.

The walls of both rooms were of kunai-grass thatch, thick and leafy, and impenetrable to light. They were not so thick, however, that deft native fingers could not rapidly fashion a peephole from the outside, and in her first weeks in the establishment May was frequently flushed, screaming indignantly, from the bathhouse, by the gaze of a dozen pairs of kindly, curious eyes framed in gaps in the thatch. The eyes were of all kinds—women's, men's and children's; and the only expression they conveyed was one of curiosity. May's antagonism to this friendly interest was supported ardently by the echoes of her suburban upbringing, and not at all mollified by the forthright self-interest which Wynfield, on leave in Sydney, had once mistaken for independence.

So now May stripped in the house and wrapped herself round with an ample bathrobe. With her husband stationed in a position commanding the best view of the bathhouse she trailed out, when she was ready, followed by a houseboy who set two lanterns to shine on the corners of the building, and then returned to his kitchen. May supervised the placing of the lanterns every night, and their location was exactly fixed where the rays would not illumine the open doorway of the dressing-room nor the high window at the end, designed to allow the air to circulate. They were hung on the trunks of trees so that the rays would not get under the building and shine upward through the bamboo rails of the shower room.

When they were placed exactly, May entered the dressing-room, shed the robe, and then got under the shower in complete darkness, and stayed there till the last drop had been drained from the container. Dripping wet, she donned the robe and floated back to the bedroom. Here, naked and starkly white, she patted herself dry and continued her preparations for the evening. When they were complete, and her skin was glowing beneath a delicate chill, she dressed in gowns that were more daring than her nudity and became, to the eye, the perfect dinner hostess, though she never saw guests in a month. The perfection was not for the mountains.

The custom was one of which she had read often, and she followed it faithfully, though in her home in Sydney it would have seemed foreign and strange. Wynfield disapproved, though he liked to change after the day's sweat. But his opinions and desires had made no impression on his wife, and her habits, once established, were unbreakable.

Dressed, May Wynfield had an undeniable beauty. It was, for a new acquaintance, so startling indeed that it hid the only two points that marred it—the hard little eyes and the prim, discontented mouth. Though, in most women, these features first focus the attention, in her they were overshadowed by the flawless complexion; the flaming red hair that, more than anything else about her, intrigued the natives; the excellent figure, a little taller than average; the good shoulders; the sinuous, yet not delicate, waist; the ample, well-shaped and not over-generous breasts; the white arms; the tapering fingers. Beneath the flowing white gown she wore nothing, and her movements emphasized long legs splendidly coupled to the graceful body.

But Wynfield had reached the stage at which the eyes, small and hard, and the lips, deceitfully fleshed, but drawn primly, overshadowed the picture.

It was an uncomfortable meal. Wynfield had trained his houseboys to be deft, but tonight Asu, partly from nervousness and partly from over-indulgence in betel nut, spilled the gravy on the linen, and Mrs. Wynfield stormed at him. Parimu, standing tall and confident in the shadows by the doorway, stepped forward quickly with a cloth ready, but in doing so he touched Mrs. Wynfield's outstretched arm, and she turned on him.

"Keep your filthy hands to yourself, convict," she screamed, and then the flood followed. Wynfield put down his knife and fork and looked at her meaningfully, trying to quiet her, but the invective went on and on.

Only when Parimu had spread a clean napkin over the damp stain, and returned with the gravy boat on its spattered plate to the kitchen did the words stop. They had no meaning. They were just invective.

Trembling, flushed, she stopped then and looked at her husband. "All right, Sebastian," she said—and when she used his given name he knew he was in for an evening of it. "Keep calm," she said, though he had said nothing. "If you'd train your niggers properly, this sort of thing wouldn't happen. Or if you'd get a transfer to a decent district. Where there's someone civilized."

"No matter where you were, you apparently couldn't learn to acquire some control in front of the boys," he said. "For God's sake, dry up."

She looked at him in some surprise. It was much too early in the pattern of their evenings of dissension for her to have raised the tiger. Usually it was bedtime before he finally gave way to the build-up of frustration, and by then her own feelings were working out, and she came easily enough to a limited reconciliation. It was a dreary, foreseeable program of antagonism, and they knew it well enough, and followed it faithfully with a kind of hopeless reluctance on Wynfield's part, and perhaps no thought at all on hers.

Tonight he abruptly broke the order of procedure. He got to his feet, left his meal on the table, and without a word to her walked to the back of the house. She waited for him to reappear. When he didn't she ate the dinner of roast pork, helping herself to more vegetables, and waited. She refilled her glass twice before she called, "Boy," and there was no reply. She walked into the back of the house, crossed the yard to the kitchen, and there was no one there. Parimu had gone and Asu. The girl Eva was nowhere to be seen. Boy-Jo, the old and wrinkled man who emptied slops and carried wood, was unaccountably absent. She had never seen the kitchen without him before. Half of the dinner was still on the tables waiting to be served, and there was already a stack of dirty dishes from the preparations and the cooking. It was obvious that Wynfield had sent everyone away.

She walked back into the dining-room where the pressure-lamp on its chain was swaying gently in the night breeze, setting swift and ungainly shadows to leaping on the patterned walls of split bamboo, and giving life to the stone axes, the sheaves of war arrows, the native drums and tables. She turned to the sideboard and poured herself a whisky. She held the glass up and looked at it, then doubled the quantity before she drank.

When Wynfield came back to the house three hours later she was sitting bolt upright at the end of the room, one hand over her mouth as she heard him coming, as though she feared a monster.

"Where the devil have you been?" she asked in a high, unnatural voice. "I was scared stiff."

"I hope to God you were scared silent," he said. In his turn, with almost exactly the same motions as she had used earlier, he went to the sideboard for a whisky. The decanter's level was low.

"They're all gone," she said accusingly. "I was all alone. Here. By myself."

"I told them to go," he said.

"Why? Why should you?"

"It's hard enough trying to give them some leadership without you making a spectacle of yourself," he said. "It degrades you, and it degrades me in their eyes. I won't have it. If it happens again I'll do the same thing."

She stood up. "You," she said. "You brought me here to the wildest country in the Territory with nothing but filthy niggers and a plane once a week that doesn't stay. God, I haven't seen a white man in four months, except you, you nigger-loving bastard. If you can call yourself a white man. Do you know what it's like sitting here, waiting, in an empty house, a thousand miles from nowhere?" Her voice rose to a scream. "Do you know? You don't, you . . ."

She picked up her skirts and ran past him swiftly, to the open door.

"Where do you think you're going?" he askd, playing calm.

She wheeled at the edge of the veranda. "I'm getting out. Out. Out," she screamed. "I'm getting out and leaving you, and never coming back, never."

"Well, there's a plane in four days," he said. "I'll bid you good-by then, with the greatest of pleasure."

"I'm going now," she said.

He put down his glass and said, "Look, be reasonable, May. You can't walk. There's no road. There's not even a track all the way. You might get to the station at Ralni, and that's as far as there is a track. You've got ninety miles to go—three good days—and on forty miles of it the bush coons still use poison on their arrows, and they still use arrows. You've seen those arrows. If you did get to Ralni you'd still have to catch the same plane, or a later one. And then you'll have started something you wouldn't be able to stop."

She essayed an imitation of his calm.

"Look, Sebastian, *dah*ling," she said viciously. "I'm getting out and the way I'll go the whole damn' world will know of it. I'm getting out. I'm getting out now."

Something in him snapped and he said, "Well, get," and turned his back on her. She stood there irresolutely for a moment, on the edge of the veranda, and then turned and walked out into the night.

How far she would have gone, no one can say. She walked past the flower-banked garden, through the fringe of imported African tulip trees, and emerged on the airfield. There was no moon, but the stars gave light, and she could see the shapes of familiar trees, and the crests of the collection of native huts farther over, across the strip. She walked hastily, her mind a red ragtag of emotion, with no coherent thought; traveling back over the conversation and feeding her anger. But it was half a mile to the end of the airstrip, and when she had reached it she had cooled.

From the end of the strip the track branched off to the right among the trees, and wound gently down a slope, two miles, zigzagging across the next valley and the one lower, to a swing-bridge on the river. It was a good track, and wide—perhaps ten feet wide, and tramped smooth as a carpet by generations of brown feet. The trees were cleared back from it a little way, and bushes of a flower with an elusive fragrance she now recognized grew at its borders, broken here and there by clumps of the tanket plant which was the peace symbol of the people.

But the trees were still close enough to cast shadows, and the movements of the night were in them, the scampering of opossums and the flight of an owl and the small noises of rodents. So she thought, then, of the emptiness ahead of her, of the little naked men armed with arrows that, being poisoned, killed swiftly; of the difficulties that Wynfield had experienced in establishing the precarious bonds of a distant friendship.

She thought, for instance, of a photograph he had shown her of a native, one of his carriers, propped up blotched, dead and swollen beside the track, with the warning of a tambu sign beside him. And then she thought of the strength Brick Wynfield had shown in his remorseless pursuit of the murderers, and that was the first time she wavered.

In her pause, she half turned, and in that moment she saw a movement in the corner of her eye, from the back of her, along the path on which she had come.

"Who's that?" she said, sharply. But there was no reply.

She walked on, then, her heart beating, and her head high. Now she was thinking wildly of the little men with the poisoned arrows, although she kept telling herself they had never been seen within twenty miles of the station. They kept to their own territory. Still, she thought of them, and their faces, thick-lipped and stupid, and their tiny bodies and their daggers of human bone and their necklaces of dogs' teeth, and the poison which dropped their victims within yards of where they had been struck.

The poison was one of the most elusive properties of the tribe. It was reputed to be a vegetable poison; and by reputation was endowed with half a dozen diabolic properties. Old New Guinea hands claimed it was used on all the war arrows. Wynfield had dozens of such arrows in his collection, and he was careful how he handled them, but no one had sent the arrows to civilization for an analysis of the poison. No one knew exactly what it was, or what it was extracted from, or whether it had an antidote. . . .

Now she was sure she heard a movement behind her, and she turned swiftly round and said, "Who's that?" but there was no reply. She was not a woman of courage. Anger and obstinacy dominant in the flaring red hatred of her mind had brought her here into danger, and the way out and the way back alike lay through danger. She said in a high strained voice, "Come out, whoever you are," taking a hesitant step toward the origin of the sound. She opened her mouth to scream when a figure stepped from the darkness of the trees. But in spite of the blackness she had the impression of a lap-lap swinging from the waist of the figure, and she knew it belonged to no wild man.

"Who is it?" she asked again, still in fear but more quietly.

"Missy," said the figure, "I think you ought to go back."

"Parimu!" She recognized the voice. It was Wynfield's personal boy, a huge man for a native, with big thighs such as all the mountainmen have, a big barrel chest, and a big-nosed, ugly face.

Now at any rate she was safe. Parimu would guard her, even though he represented all she hated, the country, the people and the way her husband devoted his life, and therefore hers, to their service.

"Get out," she spat, and knew as she did that he would not.

Parimu's voice was pleading.

"Better to go back, missy," he said again.

Anger flared up in her. "Go to hell," she said, and turned and continued walking.

This time Parimu followed close behind, silently enough, but obtrusively, and the anger mounted in her like a flame. At the brow of the spur, where the track dipped steeper, there were two openings in the trees, and she hesitated a moment, to pick the right track. Parimu's voice came again, pleading.

"Missy," he said. "I think you ought to go back." She took no notice. Before she started off again he was talking more. "It is a bad place along the track," he said. "The people will not go there in the night."

Still she took no notice. At the creek at the bottom of the hill there was a tree-trunk bridge, and she paused again, making sure of her footing. She realized suddenly she was wearing her evening slippers, and that they would not go far. Her gown was trailing and wet round her ankles.

"If missy wants to walk I will walk with her," Parimu said. "But it isn't good she should walk as far as this. Missy must go back soon, because this is too far to walk from the station."

"Shut your mouth, Parimu," she said. "Get to hell out of here."

Parimu said, "Missy can walk as far as the top of the next rise. Then she must go back or I will take her."

She had reached the farther end of the bridge and she swung round, outlined in the white gown like a marsh mist against the blackness of the hill, and the dark water rippled between them.

"Lay a hand on me, Parimu, and I'll have you hanged. I can have you hanged and I'll do it. You understand that, Parimu."

Parimu's voice was unchanged, supplicating, gentle.

"I have thought of this, missy. I know if I take you back you can bring me to a court and if I have laid hands on you, you can have me hanged. Nevertheless, it will be a thing I have to do. Perhaps Master Brick will see to it that I am safe."

"I'm telling you," she said, and her voice was cold and deadly, "I'm telling you that if you lay a hand on me you will be hanged. Master Brick will have nothing to do with it. It will go to another court and you will be hanged. Now go. Get back and leave me."

"Missy, I have thought of this too," he said. "I have thought of this and it seems if I take you back and you are not willing, it is still a thing Master Brick would have me do. It seems that if you walk, walk, walk, this will be a great shame on Master Brick. You will have brought him a great shame if you do not go back before the people are moving. And so, missy, you may walk to the top of the rise, and then I will take you back, if you will not come. But turn back now, missy."

But without a word she moved abruptly on into the darkness and began to climb the hill. When she came to the top of the rise and the track leveled out she paused, and if there had been a moon in that place, Parimu would have seen the sulky mouth in a wicked smile.

"Is this where I must stop, Parimu?" she asked, and her voice was dangerously cold.

"Please, missy," he said. "This is the place."

She waited there for a moment. There, or at the bridge, or on the hill, anger had crystallized and made a plan in her mind, and her mind was full of it. For this was the way she could strike a vicious blow at Wynfield, her husband. It was in her power, because of the strength of the man Parimu and the love he had for Wynfield, to have Wynfield hang the man, or watch another man hang Parimu for Wynfield's own default.

It was a mad plan, wicked to a degree that she could not, in any

other circumstances, have conceived; and it was a plan that would
have fallen and been rejected in a little more time. At the moment
on top of the hill it was in her mind, and at the top of the hill she
herself was, as she stood, a perversion of Death.

"Well, Parimu," she said, almost gaily, almost lightheartedly, "do
what you can. I'm on my way."

She took three steps farther down the track into the blackness
beyond. Then Parimu took her from behind, and caught her up in
his arms, as deftly as a circus performer, putting one of his great
brown arms about her shoulders and the other behind her knees,
and sweeping her clear of the ground.

And she fought. She fought silently and viciously. She rained
blows on his face, scratched her long nails down his cheek, put her
fingers through his lips and tore. She swung suddenly for her own
slipper, missed it, dropped it on the track, pulled off the other and
beat Parimu on the face with the heel. He grabbed for it, swinging
her, and took it from her and threw it in the bushes, but not before
it had brought the blood spurting from his great nose, and cut the
skin above his eye.

She lay quiet then. She had not been fighting to break away.
She had been fighting to damage him, and to leave the marks of
the damage.

Parimu began to speak, in dignity and gentleness.

"It would have been better for you to have gone back quietly,
missy," he said. "Now it is too late, but you should have gone."

She laughed at him. In that moment she could laugh, but the cold
emotion in her, the searing rage, made the laugh fanciful and forced.

"You're a dead man, Parimu," she said. "You will be hanged.
Look."

Both her hands were at the neckline of her gown. She ripped, and
the neckline tore to the belt. "Look, look, look," she screamed. The

dress tore, and tore again. She ripped the skirt from the belt, and the dress hung from her body in tatters.

"Now, you bastard, fight me," she said. She kicked and struggled, and his great hands tried to quiet her, and left marks on the whiteness of her skin; and his blood covered them both. She stopped suddenly.

"Now I will walk," she said. "Put me down."

Parimu said, "Yes, missy," and set her on her feet. Naked and marked, she looked at him, a belt of red-splotched white about her waist, and tatters hanging from it behind. On the track at her feet there was a drift of whiteness that had been the skirt of the gown. She took it up and shook it out, quite deliberately, then fastened it about her waist after the manner of a lap-lap.

"Get on your way, Parimu," she said, but Parimu stayed fast.

"Yes, missy," he said. "Missy goes first."

She stared at him for a moment, and then walked past him. Unaccountably she said, "What sort of a man do you think you are?" Then in her bare feet she marched like a soldier back along the track to the station.

On the airfield, a good way from the house, they met Wynfield. He was walking, and he carried a torch. He flashed it on her and she stood, holding her arms stiff and apart, thrusting her bare breast out in the light of the torch, standing with her feet apart like a sacrifice.

"What in God's name . . . ?" he said.

She said, "Parimu. He attacked me."

"It's not true," he said. "Get on up to the house. There'll be enough dramatics there. Parimu, you come with me."

In the darkness of the airfield, Parimu told his story and Wynfield knew that it was true.

"I am a dead man, Master Brick," Parimu said. "I am a man for hanging."

His voice was simple and honest and, not for the first time, Wynfield felt submerged in a love for the man, a deep respect, a trusting and a bond.

"It was a great deal to do for me," he said. "You have always watched for me, Parimu."

"You have watched for me, Master Brick," Parimu said. "Perhaps I was wrong, but I thought this was a thing that had to be done."

"Perhaps I can make this right," Wynfield said. "Perhaps there is something I can do."

"There is nothing you can do, for the thing went too far," Parimu said. "I am a man for hanging."

They walked back to the house, not master and man, but two men, each troubled, and each troubled with a different thought.

Wynfield said, "Parimu, there is a thing you can do. You can build up the fire and heat water, because I don't want to ask Boy-Jo while the night is so far gone. And the things that have happened must stay secret between us till the morning."

They parted then, and Wynfield went into the house, very pale, and shaking a little. His wife was in her dressing-gown. The blood streaks marked her face and her lips were bruised. He looked at her and said nothing.

"Well, Mr. Judge and Jury," she taunted him. "Would you like to see the evidence?" She opened the gown and showed him her body, bruised and marked with Parimu's blood. There were scratches there, too, and in the instant Wynfield's mind, looking for an outlet, saw they were the marks of her own nails. And her hand was torn on the heel of it where she had hit Parimu on the teeth.

"Where is that dress?"

"I rather thought you'd want that. It's hidden, and you won't find it. Not without adding more bruises to the evidence, anyway." She laughed in a high-pitched way which would have been triumphant had it not also been tainted with some of the elements of uncertainty.

"Try and get out of this one," she said. "Those rags aren't coming out of hiding till the plane comes, and I leave. This is a case you *won't* be trusted with, Mr. Patrol Officer."

"All right," said Wynfield. "You've got the cards. But you can't keep the blood on your face till Thursday. You'd better have a bath. I've got Parimu to stoke up the fire and put the water on. It shouldn't be long. In the meantime I'll get you a drink. We both need one, and I opened a new bottle while you were gone."

She stared at him curiously, and her eyes narrowed.

"So-o-o domestic," she sneered. "Why all this consideration? Why so sudden? Yes, bring me a drink. And don't dip those poisoned arrows in it."

"All right, May," he said, quite seriously. "They're not lethal, taken orally. Not as far as we know." He went from the bedroom where they were standing, and she could hear him pouring the drinks in the dining-room. Twice he looked at the big sheaf of arrows that were among the trophies in the room—shields from the other side of the mountains, and devil-masks and daggers and a set of spinning-tops from the river district, carved and ornamented and fashioned of the black shell of coconut.

He brought in four glasses and set two on his wife's dressing-table.

"I thought we might need another one," he explained.

"I certainly do," she said. "After that attack. I told you Parimu was a murderer. I knew he'd revert to type. And, just quietly, his record won't help him any."

"That will be enough of that," he said sharply. He left the room abruptly, his drinks untasted. He was away five minutes, and he came back without an explanation, but carrying the bottle.

"Parimu has nerves of steel," he said. "He's not showing a thing, except for goose flesh on his arms. You know the way he goes. By the way," he continued conversationally, "this is the end, you know, between you and me."

She set down her glass. "You're taking this too damned quietly," she said. "I wish I knew what was going on in that head of yours. I wish I knew what you were thinking."

"I'm not thinking a thing," he said. "As a matter of fact, I'm feeling sick. I'm a bit dazed, I suppose. I couldn't have thought any woman would do it. Have another drink. We won't have many more together."

She looked at him thoughtfully. "I did nothing but go for a walk," she said. "I was attacked. Without provocation."

"Well, leave it for now."

Wynfield left her after that drink and came back after half an hour to report the bath was ready. He had set out the lanterns himself, where she always had them set, so that they cast no trace of illumination into the bathhouse. She got up immediately and went out, and Wynfield followed her as though the night were full of people, and took up his position by the door of the house, where he could watch the lanterns. She went into the dressing-room, threw off her gown, and walked the familiar few steps to the shower. At the connecting door, something stabbed into the flesh of her calf, and she jumped.

She stood stock-still for a moment, then rushed outside and snatched up the nearest lantern. She carried it back into the dressing-room and stared at the doorway between the rooms. It was lined with half a dozen arrows, set four or five inches apart, each lashed to one of the bamboos of the shower-room floor and pointing upward at a forty-five degree angle. She shifted the lantern and looked at her leg, where a deep but tiny purple wound was oozing an imperceptible trickle of blood.

Then scream after scream broke the silence of the night.

Wynfield found her lying limp and still on the floor, perhaps thirty seconds later. He set the lantern upright, then cut the lashings that fastened the arrows to the floor and pushed them aside. He stripped rapidly and pulled his wife's body with him under the shower, and in the darkness washed her hair and her face and her body until he thought that all of Parimu's blood was gone and the water was all run away. He could feel the tiny wound on her hand, the only imperfection on its flawlessness, and he thought that this could well have caused the tetanus to which he would attribute the death.

When he came back into the dressing-room he saw Parimu standing there.

"She is dead," he said. "I found her under the shower."

"Yes, Master Brick," said Parimu.

Wynfield stood at the door a moment. The night was still, and the people across the airfield had not been aroused. The roar of the waterfall came to his ears, as though at that moment it had been brought into existence, and from the orchard came the scent of citrus flowers.

Parimu followed him to the veranda, and stood by him. Wynfield, his nerves starting to shriek beneath the skin, waited a moment and dropped into the old packing-case chair. As he did so he noticed that Parimu held the sheaf of arrows in his hand, and he reached out to take them.

"Thank you, Parimu," he said. "I had forgotten them entirely. It didn't matter. I killed her. I'll have to take what's coming. I was a fool to think I wouldn't."

"Missy is dead," Parimu answered. "Yet I think many men have died by hanging for less than she did. I think she deserved to die. I have not seen you hesitate before to order the death of someone who deserved to die."

Wynfield looked at him. "I was the Government then," he said. "But now I am a man, and for myself I may not kill. It makes all the difference, Parimu."

"You did not kill her, Master Brick," Parimu said. He reached forward quickly and took the sheaf of arrows from Wynfield's limp hand. With a swift movement he bent his left knee, pulling aside his lap-lap with his left hand, and thrust the point of all five arrows through the flesh of his heavy thigh. Two of the heads splintered and broke, the other three entered beneath the skin. Wynfield jumped to his feet. "Parimu!" he cried. "Parimu, you fool!"

Parimu smiled and spoke soothingly, as to a baby. "I will not die, Master Brick, because I do not fear death. The poison of the arrows is dead. They will not hurt. Look again." He took one of the two broken points and began gently to poke it beneath the skin of the inner part of his left arm. Little streams of blood were running down his leg.

"Missy thought death was something of importance, and therefore she died," he said. "It is something-nothing. And the arrows are something-nothing. I will not die, Master Brick. Missy died of fear. She died of a great fright."

"And yet I killed her," Wynfield said.

"Did you kill her by magic?" Parimu asked. "Does the Government admit of killing by magic? Her leg was scratched, and that's all. So I think, Master Brick, she killed herself."

He pulled at the three shafts still protruding from his leg. They pulled away, leaving the heads in the wound. Deftly, he worked at them, and extracted two, but the third broke in the flesh, as its savage artificer had intended.

"Stay here, and I'll get the forceps," Wynfield said. He went into the bedroom carrying one of the arrowheads with him, and when he was out of sight he bent, and, precisely at the point where May's leg had been scratched, he thrust the hard wooden point into his leg. There was the sharp pain of penetration, and nothing more. He found the forceps, extracted the point, and went out to the waiting Parimu.

The Woman
Molak

T HE Reverend John MacAllister was brash enough to poke an ecclesiastical nose into dozens of matters that didn't concern him, a fact that, incidentally, made his life too busy for him to bother with an analysis of his errors. He had acquired his brashness in his extreme youth, and he let it have free rein after he took over the mission at Bohigi, a big river village in the Sepik district in the north of New Guinea. He saw himself here as guide, philosopher and friend to the numerous native inhabitants of his enormous parish, but he applied a very autocratic definition to the terms.

Perhaps the brashest thing he ever did was to persuade his only white neighbor, the trader Fiddle Wittner, into marriage, and even he was surprised when he won the campaign in the first round. Fiddle immediately and enthusiastically agreed with him. But when the padre turned to the poor benighted heathen girl who had shared Fiddle's bed for the past eighteen years and broke the joyous news that she could now marry her protector, he struck an immediate and unforeseen snag.

For Molak flatly refused to have anything to do with the proposal.

Even more disconcerting was the fact that she didn't look up from the game of Lucky she was playing on the floor in the corner of Fiddle's big living-room, dealing the worn cards to Fiddle's sixteen-year-old eldest and a couple of her kinsmen whom Fiddle employed casually round the house. Not even the suggestion of legitimizing her four children appealed to her, though the Reverend John explained the concept at some length, wiping an inordinate amount of sweat from his fresh young forehead with a neatly monogrammed linen handkerchief.

"Better this way," said Molak in the English she preferred to pidgin, and enunciated in a sweet low voice that had once thrilled better men than Fiddle. She answered often enough and sweetly enough to persuade the Reverend John she was not being deliberately rude, but she also made it fairly definite that she was much more interested in her incomprehensible card game than she was in the welfare of her immortal soul.

Finally the padre gave up and left the house, strolling very slowly to the river where Fiddle was anointing a new native-built canoe with red-lead in the afternoon shade of the riverbank trees.

"Mrs. Wittner objects to the ceremony," the padre said. "I find it very hard to understand. . . . I had no idea. . . . I mean I would have thought. . . .

Fiddle concentrated his attention on working the brush bristles into the deep-carved head of a crocodile which adorned the canoe bows. When it became obvious that the Reverend John was without words to express himself, he helped out.

"She's got a mind of her own," he said.

"You must send her away," decided the padre, dictatorial as ever.

Fiddle thought awhile over that. He said, "She was here before me. I'm not sure that she'd go."

"It mustn't go on. It's a terrible example to the people," said the

Reverend John. "In the interests of the community she should leave your house."

"You could suggest it to her," said Fiddle, an equable man for all the lined grimness of his face. When he looked up at the end of the sentence the padre could have sworn there was a momentary twinkle in his eyes.

"It's an abomination," said the Reverend John, his gorge rising. He was new to the islands. "It's a stink in the nostrils the way you are living. You ought to have consideration for the fact that the people regard you as head of the community. They all look up to you. If you can't control Mrs.—this woman, you should get out yourself."

Fiddle carefully squeegeed the paint brush and balanced it on the edges of the pot.

"That's hardly reasonable, padre," he said. "I've been here a long time. I don't reckon we do the people much harm, Molak and me. They've got kinda used to us, and they never knew anything better before. On the other hand, you haven't been here so very long yourself. You might be able to get round Molak after a bit. Far as I'm concerned I'll marry the girl the day she wants me to, but I won't walk out, and I don't think she will. Better leave it for awhile and try again."

"You ask me to procrastinate, to overlook the presence of evil," protested the padre. "Never put off till tomorrow the things you can do today," he quoted, but his eyes were puzzled.

That night Fiddle Wittner laughed aloud into his third rum. Behind him, bare-breasted Molak, padding silently past on her naked feet, paused at the back of his chair and placed her fingers gently on the nape of his neck, running the tips of them up into the soft fair curls. It was an unobtrusive gesture, even though there were no others to see it, and Fiddle acted as though he were unaware of it.

"The padre told me I should go away," he said when he set the rum down.

Molak smiled sweetly and said nothing. But her confidence was eloquent and apparently not at all impaired by the fact that Fiddle had left her before. She had been a young thing, not in the least aged by her two happy, naked, half-white babies, when Fiddle first went to Sydney, and Fiddle himself was in his early thirties. Before that he had never seen a white city, or, for that matter, a white country. He had been born in the islands and never imagined anything better.

That first trip to Sydney coincided with the last piping days of the uneasy peace, when the rumble of tanks on Czechoslovakian roads raised only faint echoes beyond those new and shaky borders. And Fiddle was rich with the accumulation of a lifetime spent in the islands, with a bank account growing so fast that the debits set down for the occasional case of rum, the new rifle, the launch engine and the other small European necessities of his life hardly checked its growth. In his small way, Fiddle was a king, and though his kingdom would never have been accounted wealthy the costs of its administration were negligible, and small streams of wealth flowed intermittently in from many directions.

On the steamer, among planters and vaguely familiar Government men on furlough, and the round-trip tourists who represented an entirely new race, Fiddle was amazed to discover the numbers of fascinating new ways in which money could be spent. He came to the swift conclusion that he had been missing things. Less justifiable was the opinion he rapidly formed that he was attractive to women.

But it was understandable. A typist spending the savings of five uneventful years on two months of Pacific heaven showed a marked preference for his company on an otherwise lonely boat-deck as well as in the lounge-bar and other spots perhaps less accessible; and she never found it necessary to explain her motives to him. And a wealthier, older woman, traveling with her sister in search of some

relief from the drabness of a country store and her husband, its pro-
prietor, made a brave attempt to displace the typist without achieving
anything but an extended range of vision for all three.

Luckily for Fiddle, neither of these sirens was headed for Sydney.
The typist stayed there briefly, long enough to give him an introduction to an expensive night-club, and after that Fiddle was on his
own, in a colloquial rather than a technical manner of speaking.

Others swam into the picture, attracted mainly by Fiddle's
charming and ingenuous way of carrying a proportion of his wealth
in small rolls of fifties. And Fiddle learned things: such items of
intelligence as that an orchestra, under the baton of an approach-
able leader, would play any item the girl-friend wanted, and that
this had its effect on the girl-friend; that a friendly head-waiter could
contrive an excellent table in the best situation on an otherwise
crowded floor; that a taxi-driver could be persuaded, for a consideration, to give away the night's prospects and become a general
factotum and message boy of a superior kind.

He discovered also the comfort of superior lodgings and good
cuisine, of twenty-four-hour good company that could and would
take a dismissal as equably as Molak and still flatter his ego on subsequent occasions. He discovered the attractions of race-tracks and
cruising yachts, of gymnasiums and tiled pools and massage-benches.
He reveled in every luxury the islands men had ever mentioned in
their after-furlough braggings, and considerably more of luxury than
any of these had been able to afford.

So it was not surprising that when the most fluid of his vanishing
fortunes had disappeared altogether, and he had consequently returned to the islands, the seat of his kingdom no longer looked so
pleasant. The food no longer tasted as it had, and the experiment
he made of importing a couple of cases of good wines was not a
success. There was seldom anyone to share the bottle, for Molak
still ate in her corner; and anyway, he preferred the strong warmth

of Queensland rum. His bed, with the surrounding air stilled to occlusion by the mosquito-net, was not so fresh as that in the spring-tinted rooms in which he had woken to a Sydney morning consciousness. The jungle drums offered no substitute for the sophisticated rhythms of a swing band; the lap-laps of his table boys were less flattering to the eye than the stiff shirts of waiters perhaps less deft.

And Molak was no longer even Molak; for he had lost her to momentary illusions of a redhaired, gay and saucy chit of a Sydney companion whose name, surprisingly, was Myrtle. Those blue eyes of Myrtle's, those chiseled nostrils, that hair which, loosed of restraint, massed into a glory on a cushion or a pillow-slip, the body he had never been able to command nor ever forget were all within his arms on a hundred nights. And then there would be only Molak, and she less than Molak, because she was never in his vision.

So Fiddle laid long-range plans for a second holiday, during the course of which he hoped to reorganize and reconstitute his subsequent life. In his preparations he nursed his income back to a thriving state, scraping every shilling and conserving equipment. He negotiated to send the elder children to school in Queensland. And when all his other dispositions were at last complete he sent for Molak and told her that their life together was at an end.

She took it very well, he thought, looking him squarely in the eyes and saying nothing except words of acceptance. She made it very easy for him and when he left he cursed her without knowing why. He left her well provided for, and she needed very little. And then Sydney was ahead of him.

But it was farther away than he had thought. Two days after he had caught his ship, while they were at sea, the radio brought in the news of Pearl Harbor and Malaya. There was a new era opening in the islands.

Fiddle Wittner, being of normal courage and not irrevocably tied to any immediate future of his own planning, left the ship at Port

Moresby and, after a very few days of form-filling and waiting, found himself a member of the coast-watchers, a unit in which the sterling service he later performed was taken as normal by an unimpressed bunch of fellow heroes.

He got to Sydney eventually at the beginning of 1943. Naturally, he was still in the service, and he had a couple of training-courses to attend, but he had time on his hands and a good spell of leave, and he enthusiastically took up his island plans at the stage at which he had laid them down. He wanted a wife who was white, charming, pert and preferably redheaded. He wanted her beautifully dressed and well turned out, so he started where he could find an opening.

He looked for her in the night-clubs, which he found rather more populous than formerly. He also found that head-waiters no longer had tables reserved against his coming unless he had made previous arrangements; that taxi-drivers were less accommodating, and that band-leaders had long lists of required selections ahead of his.

He could have overcome the worst of these difficulties by flashing the tens (fifties were out of print) he carried in his well-lined pockets. But the war had made his future look very insecure, and there was the matter ahead of him of impressing a prospective bride, a business for which Fiddle was convinced he needed money—he had little presence and few civilized abilities.

In his second week he met a dark little charmer called Nita, but after three nights she ditched him for an American Army major, and though he saw her again, he was resentful. He drifted from one place to another, more and more unhappily; walking, as often as not, because of the taxis that speeded past his uniform to where something in American olive-drab raised a beckoning finger from the curb ahead.

Dolly was an army girl he met in his second month. She was tall and she was lovely, and, best of all, she had red hair. She was a good companion and accommodating, and Fiddle enjoyed his every moment with her. Except that he couldn't get used to her uniform, stiff and masculine, making perversions of tendernesses and discouraging contacts. Dolly's other belongings ran to an evening dress with accessories—an outfit she sometimes swapped with barracks-mates —swimsuits, and that was all. Fiddle decided that his opportunity had arrived.

His ways were his alone. For all his recent experience of the world his plan of campaign was that of a lad in his late adolescence. At an early stage of the association he got all her physical measurements, a rather cunning strategy this, carried out with the bluff friendly transparency of a man from the bush. He compared her, to her advantage, with the current newspaper beauties whose proportions were listed in detail in the Sunday sheets, and, thus armed, he started shopping.

Without telling her anything about it he bought Dolly a whole trousseau, silk nightgowns and negligees, underclothes of a texture he wouldn't have believed existed but for his previous Sydney experience, shoes and handbags and jewelry. He topped off his purchases with a rather magnificent diamond, set in a ring of which the measurement was the only guess he made. He had the trousseau delivered to his room in rather charmingly matched traveling cases, and with the ring in his pocket, set out to find Dolly.

It was a bad night. Outside the hotel he had the luck to stop a taxi, but as he laid his hand on the door-handle the driver leaned toward him. "Sorry, mate, I'm booked," he said. At the same time he reached over and opened the back door for two young American officers who had come up behind Fiddle's back. Fiddle waited unsuccessfully for twenty minutes, and it rained as he began to walk. He found Dolly rather cool; and later, when he produced the ring for her, she laughed in his face.

In the morning he put most of his possessions into storage, and immediately set about hastening his return to the field. He was successful in getting his transfer through in something less than a week, and from then onward he devoted his whole ability to his lonely duties.

He didn't see Molak again until after the war. She was in the crowd which welcomed him back to the village; not in the forefront, nor yet hiding at the back, but with others of the women a little aside, and she smiled at him, her eyes open and honest. Later, when he had opened the house, he went into the village and found her. The war had aged her very little. She was still upright and well built, not thin anywhere and not over-nourished. Her skin glowed with a bronze beauty that was properly youth's.

He said, "You will come back to the house," and she assented without surprise and without expressed pleasure.

When she was there she asked him, "When will the white missus come?"

He answered, "There is no white missus"; and that was all that was said.

It was years before Fiddle thought of the luggage in storage in Sydney, and he sent for it more as a whim to awaken old memories than for the value that was in it, for the bill he had to pay seemed more than its worth. The night it arrived he got very drunk on rum and went through the matched suitcases intended for Dolly, holding each fragile item up to the light and presenting it, one piece at a time, to Molak.

She was pleased, he thought, and that night they had a great deal of joy in each other, Molak, unlike the others of her tribe, being almost Polynesian in this attribute. But in the morning Molak appeared still in her lap-lap without the clothes and the ornaments and the jewelry except for simple gold half-moons of earrings. When he went to the village later Fiddle saw why.

Every woman in the place was wearing something that had been once intended for a redhaired bride—a brassière, or silk panties, or

a slip, or a trailing chiffon negligee. Some wore flaming brooches
in their lap-laps or, incongruously, in their short-clipped frizzy hair.
Even the men shared; the luckier ones carrying handbags.

Molak never said anything to Fiddle about her lavish distribution
of his gifts, and Fiddle, after days of consideration, said nothing to
Molak. But he never again had the vision of white faces, white at-
tributes in his association with her. His love-making was with Molak
and not with some substitute for a redhaired, faraway beauty.

And gradually the dainty, light little pieces of textile nonsense
wore themselves out, or were relegated to other uses, such as
making strainer-cloths for the sago. They were not, after all, very
useful in that climate.

But there were still a few of the women wearing the clothes when
the Reverend John McAllister first came to the village, a young
missionary in his first executive appointment; and he asked Fiddle
then where the clothes had come from.

"Trade goods," said Fiddle, and the padre reflected aloud on the
ridiculous choice of stock made by some amateur traders.

He had been three or four months in office before he first tried
to persuade Molak into marriage with the amenable Fiddle; and he
didn't readily accept failure. He tried again and again to get her to
see the light, but she would have none of his arguments. After each
attempt the Reverend John came to talk it over with Fiddle.

"There's another matter," he said once. "If you could persuade
her to wear clothing a little more adequate I would be most grateful. The other women follow her lead, you know, to a great extent.
I've managed to persuade some of the girls to wear their blouses—
I don't like them called Mother Hubbards; it's an ignominious term
—but most of them just won't listen to me."

Fiddle looked doubtful. "Not sure that I like them, padre."

"It's not a matter of liking. It's a matter of morals," said the
Reverend John severely.

"You go right ahead then," suggested Fiddle. "But you won't make her wear them. She just doesn't like clothes above the waist. You talk to her."

"Perhaps if you bought her some. . . ." pleaded the Reverend John.

"Not even if I did," said Fiddle. "I bought her some once and she just wouldn't wear them."

"A most remarkable woman," said the Reverend John, shaking his head. "Most remarkable."

The Dark
of the Moon

TOMBO's corpse was the first that Eve Maybrick
had seen; but it was not that of itself which
shocked her so deeply. It was the agony of the
face, lined and drawn and strangely swollen under the chin, the eyes
wide and staring in an excess of disbelief and terror.

The limbs were not at all discomposed, except as the villagers had
put them, with the arms folded, the knees drawn up on the bamboo
stretcher; for Tombo had been a long time dying. He had been six
days dying, six days in which his death was written; and the gaunt
waste that had been Tombo's fine and well-developed body less than
a week before shocked her too.

She turned to her companion while the wailing women watched
her from the corners of their weeping eyes, their heads bent over
their nursing children, their hands touching the corpse, fondling it,
resting on it, as many as could manage unobtrusively.

"Well, that's what witchcraft can do," Sommers said. "Let's get
out of here."

They passed by the men, weeping a little apart from the women
and covering their greased bodies with the white wood ashes from

their cooking fires in token of their mourning, and walked over toward the parsonage.

Maybrick was waiting on the veranda, his puny body covered completely, in spite of the heat, with long khaki trousers and a white shirt buttoned at collar and cuffs.

The two men looked like members of alien races—Sommers tall, heavy for his height, soldier-straight, unshaved yet unable even to stand still without a mental swagger; Maybrick delicate and tender-fleshed, a small man with a high-domed forehead, chubby cheeks, a man personable enough and friendly, but a pale wraith of a messenger to carry the Word of God into the wild hills.

Maybrick said, "Hello, Mr. Sommers. We've seen nothing of you for months. You've been seeing about your houseboy—very sad. We did what we could, but it had no effect. A most mysterious thing. The people say witchcraft. Everything is witchcraft. Sangguma, sangguma, they say. I thought I had a convert in your Tombo. I thought he had a true belief, but he died. He's been here a week, and I couldn't do anything. He came last Wednesday."

"They kill themselves," Sommers said.

"Yes; well, it's nearly a week ago he came in. I spoke to him, and it was just as if he couldn't hear me. He seemed to be trying to say something, but he couldn't talk. He just got worse and worse, and yesterday he died. I thought you might have come over earlier. I thought you might know what to do."

"Nothing you can do," said Sommers. "These coons kill themselves. I thought Tombo was safe. He's from Aitape, and I thought he wouldn't know the local conventions yet. But they die just the same. Just scare themselves to death."

Eve shuddered, remembering the vacuous stare that still mirrored the utmost in horror in the dead man's face.

"What was he doing to walk in the dark of the moon?" she asked sharply.

"Do you think that had anything to do with it?" Sommers countered. "As a matter of fact he was doing something for me. I sent him on a message. I could feel a bit guilty, I suppose. If it were witchcraft he died of."

"It's the same story they told us when we came," Eve said. "They told us no one could walk in the dark of the moon. And on the night of the new moon. They said that sangguma would get anyone who did. They said he would return to the village on the next night but he wouldn't talk. That he would be tired but couldn't sleep. That he would have things to say but couldn't speak. He would be hungry and couldn't eat; and he would seek comfort and couldn't listen. And that he would die within a week. That's exactly what they told us. And that's exactly what Tombo did. It was horrible."

"Oh, well . . ." Sommers said. But Eve cut in again quickly. Normally she didn't talk much. This was a flood to drown her feelings.

"I saw him when he came the first day, in the late afternoon," she said. "He was walking like a man in a trance. He didn't take any notice of anything; but once or twice he would walk up to some of the men. They were in groups, you know, standing round; and everyone was very silent. They seemed to have expected it. Tombo would shake his head from side to side, and his eyes would be staring and he would say nothing. The men would watch him and say nothing.

"And I was watching once when he stopped and put his arm round young Ratu. Ratu is Joanna's child. He's about three. And Ratu screamed and ran. And Tombo stayed there with his arm outstretched, and he looked puzzled and horrified and worn out all at once. He looked terrible. But his body was fit and well. His face was drawn—but that corpse doesn't even look like him. And that was only five-six days ago."

A house-girl came out with a tray of tea things, her rolypoly brown face beaming above a spotless white Mother Hubbard that was pushed most absurdly out of shape by her strong and well-formed breasts.

Eve busied herself with a small cane table, and Sommers watched her. He was a lusty man; and Eve satisfied his eye. Her red-brown hair, her green eyes, pale skin, trim figure were appetizers to his hunger, and her movements were rhythmic, wasting no effort. She caught his look and flushed, but Sommers didn't turn away. There was nothing sensitive about him.

He excused himself after awhile, and, despite protests from Maybrick, readied himself for the long walk back to his house.

Maybrick sounded over-enthusiastic with his invitations to stay the night, Eve thought. She supported him in them only to the extent that politeness indicated, hoping fervently that Sommers wouldn't accept; hoping also that his infrequent visits would never coincide with her husband's self-imposed patrols which took him away sometimes for a week or more.

But Maybrick's self-reliance, never firmly founded, had received a jolt from the outbreak of witchcraft in the village which he thought he had made into a little stronghold of Methodism. He craved male companionship, subconsciously seeking a lead he could follow.

Nearly all his tiny flock were paying their pagan homage through the corpse to its destroyer, swept at this single blow from their newer religious solace of which the visible symbol was the great kunai-grass barn of a church that Maybrick had erected: a barn too ambitious for the materials of its making, for it lurched drunkenly now by the side of the village road.

"Come again soon, Mr. Sommers," Maybrick called as his visitor opened the picket-gate. "And next time stay awhile. The house is yours at any time."

Sommers waved a farewell with his stick, and set out along the path, striding heel-and-toe like a city hiker in the freshness of early morning.

It was dark when he reached his own house, but the lamps were lit. Tombo's widow, a pretty little dark woman, squatted on the floor by an inner door, dealing from a tattered deck of cards to two youngsters. Unlike Maybrick's servants she wore only a lap-lap; and her bared breasts were pleasant to look at. She got up hurriedly as Sommers came in, and went out to the kitchen. The two boys stayed on the floor.

The woman came out almost immediately with a bottle of rum, a jug of water and a tray of ice. Sommers mixed himself a drink and took it out on the veranda.

The house lay at the top of his domain, a section of steeply sloping hillside. Sommers had bought the land from the natives at the cost of two years' time, an infinite patience in negotiation and a small capital outlay. He preferred it to the richer bottom land in the valley, because some day he hoped to start a tea plantation. The prospects were ideal. It was better land and just as well situated as that on which tea plantations had already been established in the Central Highlands, three or four hundred miles away; the altitude was ideal, he was close to cheap sources of labor, and transport problems were not insuperable. But he needed capital for drying-sheds, for packaging and shipping equipment and for a nursery. The plantation would be a winner when it started, but he was in no hurry. He could wait.

In the meantime he had the house, and he supported himself by labor-recruiting trips for other enterprises. He had his own efficient ways of handling natives. They feared him, for one thing. And the headmen of the villages where he was known found it politic to keep friendly with him. So he did a steady trade in labor for the plantations, and made sufficient money for his wants.

He watched the hillside under the young moon, imagining it as it would look when the young tea bushes replaced the forest. At least he tried, deliberately, to conjure up that picture, but in spite of himself his thoughts turned toward the missionary's wife.

"Beba," he called; and a voice answered from one of the three huts clustered against the thin mountain bush at the edge of the clearing.

"Yes, master. Coming, master."

The boy hurried to the veranda.

"Come up here," Sommers said. And waited till the boy mounted the steps and stood beside his chair.

"You've got a lot of friends at the village, Beba," Sommers said, speaking fluent pidgin in the fast native fashion. "Suppose that you waited for word of something you wanted to know. Now a friend with a flute or a drum could let you know—not a big drum that would tell everyone. A little drum, speaking a message that no one else would know the meaning of. Right?"

"Yes, master," Beba said.

"Well, suppose the missionary goes away for a walkabout—a long walkabout, two-three days a week; I'd like to know. You must tell me, without fail. But don't stay at the village yourself—I want you here. You find a friend in the village to let me know. Understand?"

"Yes, master."

"Now this isn't a thing for talking about. I want no talk in the village. And I want no talk here. Especially no talk to Kardu. Not now or after. Otherwise . . ." He lifted up his fist in front of his face and clenched it. Beba just said: "Yes, master," again, in a matter-of-fact way and waited.

"That's all," said Sommers. "Now get."

He watched until Beba had re-entered his hut and then raised his voice again.

"Kardu."

After a moment the little dark woman was at his side, in silence.

He looked at her keenly.

"You're still playing cards?"

"Yes, master." The words were the same as Beba's, the intonation soft and gentle.

"Get me some more ice, and then get to bed. I'll be in when the moon goes down."

Kardu turned without a word, and without a change of expression. Sommers knew that he would find her lying awake beneath his bed, waiting for his next call. She was very amenable, and she put on none of the airs most native girls assumed when they were elevated to the position of a white man's mistress.

But for the first time since he had stolen her from his houseboy he could find no interest in Kardu that night. She had intrigued him in the past to the point where he had sent Tombo her husband on a fruitless errand—as it happened, to his death; but that part of it was purely accidental. And he had been firm about allowing that death to have no influence at all in his continuing relations with the girl.

Quite suddenly now, within a week, he had lost all interest in her. It was the white woman. He wanted her; and he would do a lot to get her.

Beba brought him no message in the days that followed, and his desire grew mightily. He fed it by calling a couple of times at the mission in the village, and after each occasion he fancied he was making progress. Maybrick liked him—that was obvious. And Eve seemed to be glad of his additional company.

He thought the time to strike was soon. In the meantime his temper was shortening and the little Kardu took the brunt of it uncomplainingly.

It was three weeks after his instruction to Beba when, as he drowsed in his chair in the evening, a movement disturbed him, and he looked up to find the boy standing beside him. He had heard nothing. No sounds of drums or flute. Not even a footstep. But Beba was there.

"Master?"

"What is it?"

"The drum talked, master. The parson has gone. He has gone up the valley and will be gone tomorrow and the next day. Perhaps longer; perhaps not."

"Right," said Sommers. "Now get out."

He got up quickly and went into his room. He picked up his revolver belt and a flashlight; and came out strapping the belt round his waist. Beba was still by the steps.

"Master?"

"Something else?"

"Master, the moon is dark again. This is the first night of the dark of the moon."

It was unexpected, and Sommers hesitated. But only for a moment.

"I've got eyes in my head," he said. "Now go, if you haven't anything else to say."

Beba walked across to the huts without a word, and Sommers cut down into the track and plunged into the thick gloom of the bush. He knew the trail, but he used the flashlight fairly constantly. He was ten minutes from the clearing when he heard two clear notes of a flute. The sound seemed to come from the clearing; and from somewhere it was answered.

Sommers stood stock-still for a moment, unreasonably angry that anyone should keep a check on his movements—if the two notes represented a message, as seemed likely. He hadn't heard any flute before, and there must have been a purpose in the call and the answer. But he had no desire to retrace his steps up the steep hill, he was urgently committed to his immediate desires, and after a moment he went on.

When he descended to creek level and crossed the swing-bridge, the bush changed character. Taro grew above the bank; and in the air was the faint sweet scent of gora-gora, the ginger lily, which clustered in clumps eight feet high. The bush was more tangled and diverse, broken here and there by stands of the giant bamboo, now rustling and groaning and moaning in the light breeze. The creepers reached down into the water of the creek, and there were stirrings among the leaves. The bush grew darker, and Sommers kept his flashlight on constantly, more acutely conscious with every moment of the noises of the night.

But there's no noise of the forest night that says, "Master."

It was soft and sibilant. But it was an order, not a supplication. Sommers swung in his tracks, and played the flashlight along the way he had come. His revolver had leaped to his hand. He slipped the safety-catch off and fingered the trigger, feeling comfort in it; almost fondling it, as a baby will fondle fur.

Now the sound was ahead of him. Soft yet sharp. And in the same . . . or in another voice? He swung again, and this time he fancied he saw the movement of a shadow and fired immediately. The night noises ceased, and to the right of him a voice said, "Master."

He started to walk on down the track, and a blunt-headed arrow took the flashlight from his hand. He yelled and swung and shot, then scrambled frantically for the flashlight.

And as he picked it up a voice in front of him said, "Master."

He fired three shots quickly then. But it must have been half an hour before he fired the last. He was at screaming-pitch then.

And all that answered him was the same whisper: "Master."

But as that last shot belted into a tree trunk he went down under a rush of soft brown bodies.

He went down and he went out. He could not have been out for long; but when he came to he was in a strange clearing. It did not lie on the track, and he had never seen it before.

There was a small fire burning in the clearing, and there were men about him, and some carried torches of the fronds of coconut palms. What men they were he didn't know. They wore painted bark masks over their faces, and little else. They were armed and ornamented, and they were silent.

He himself was naked, and unmarked. There was not a stitch of his clothes anywhere; nor did anyone have his revolver or his flashlight, so far as he could see.

He couldn't take much stock of his situation, because he was in an excess of terror and because the moment his eyes opened the voices began.

This time they said, "Dance, master."

They were the same voices, and they came at him the same way as they had in the dark, now from this side of the circle, now from that. He was on his feet. His arms were bound, and he hesitated.

An arrow thudded into the ground by his foot, and from the other side of the circle a voice insisted: "Dance, master."

He lifted his foot, and danced in the native way, but shuffling. And the natives danced with him; and when he hesitated and slowed down they said, "Dance, master"; but otherwise they were silent. There was a throbbing that he thought was drums, but it seemed more a vibration than a sound. And he danced—and danced.

In the course of the dance, from time to time, they practiced indignities on him, of several kinds. But he had lost all cohesion in his mind. He couldn't even promise himself revenge, because somehow he knew there would be no revenge.

The indignities and the upsurge of his feelings exhausted him, and he felt consciousness leaving him as he toppled. But when he came back to life again he was on his feet. And his feet were dancing.

Some time later he discovered that his arms were not bound, but he was not relieved. He had no feeling in this matter, nor in any.

The tempo of the dance increased and increased. He was caught up in it, wedded to it, one with it. But from time to time great waves of blackness seemed to engulf him, sometimes not quite, and sometimes utterly.

It was from one of these blackouts that he awoke to find himself in the village street. There was no dance, no drum-beat. He was staggering like a man dying of thirst in a desert, or as such a man is pictured, and it was a dead and unreal world.

He couldn't even think it was the village. The thing had the qualities of a nightmare. There was no sound at all, a complete and utter absence of sound. There was sight, unreal vision which seemed to have no depth. But there was no sound.

The villagers were standing in groups, looking at him; and they looked as though they, too, were horrified.

He went up to the nearest group to speak to them. He did speak, but his tongue was motionless in his mouth, and no sound came. He put his hand on the nearest man's chest, and it was warm and living. The man was shrinking back, and he slapped the chest hard, but the slap gave no sound.

He wandered from one group to another. He stopped still and looked at himself. He was naked still. His feet were bleeding, not badly. His hands and wrists and his shoulders and his belly were all scratched, and here and there bleeding slightly. These were all wounds from the creepers in the bush. Except for them he had no mark on him.

Yet he was a living pain; dead tired and racked with pain. He was not sure that he could remember the village. He was not sure that he was in it; or that it was not nightmare. He was not sure that the village existed. He couldn't really remember himself: who he was, or what he did. He could remember that there was something he wanted in this silent village, and he staggered on, aimlessly, in circles.

Then he saw the church, reeling on its piles by the flower-bordered road, and it reminded him of something, and he went inside.

It was there that Eve Maybrick found him: a zombie, another Tombo, one of the walking dead.

"Six days," she thought. "I've got six days to save him."

Not once did it occur to her that that was an abnegation of her faith. She sent a messenger after Maybrick; but he would be already returning, probably, by the time the messenger reached him. And she sent another down the valley to the settlement; but that was a week's walk.

Maybrick came back in two more days.

As it happened, Sommers didn't have six days. He had little more than three. After Maybrick came back, the little missionary prayed for Sommers. That was all he could do. And on the following night at midnight, Sommers died.

The Maybricks are good religious people who hold to their faith, but at their mission they do not walk about in the dark of the moon. And they avoid the subject of witchcraft.

For in all the three days, Sommers didn't speak. So he couldn't tell them of the little brown men in the masks who ruled the dark nights.

And not even he knew of the sago spines—the two-inch needles administered mercifully under the anaesthetic of exhaustion. He was buried with them—two in his ears that had pierced his eardrums so that he couldn't hear; two through the base of his tongue so he couldn't eat, couldn't talk; and two under the scratched skin of his belly so that he would die within a week.

The Road
to Heaven

TO the village of Susuba, in the delta of the
Watumba River, first came these two, the missionary and the patrol officer. They were of
Susuba, yet alien to it; the one striving for its spiritual domination,
the other carrying the flag of Government and assuming its temporal leadership. Behind Susuba, in the darkly forested reaches of
the river, new fields for both of them stretched forever back to the
mountains, peopled thinly with small and honest communities of
primitive men—Melanesians whose contacts with other people had
been few, and often furious. They were New Guinea people, little
men who, throughout their lives, sought peace and stood to their
weapons; simple people whose reactions returned a smile for a
smile and a flight of arrows for a hostile gesture.

For them, the white race was concentrated in Susuba, in the
persons of Carl Vandenburg, the patrol officer, and the Reverend
William Sanders.

As examples to the people, they had been well chosen.
They were both young, both active, both vigorous and strong in
their beliefs. Each contained the material of leadership. Each had
a belief in himself and the things he represented, and therefore

251

each commanded ready allegiance, swift co-operation, and even devotion among the people. But each was impatient and intolerant of the other's beliefs, and for a long time there was an antagonism, a warring of wills.

To imagine them, however, as being alone in the village of Susuba, each solitary in his own sphere of domination, would be wrong. Vandenburg, the patrol officer, had first of all the backing of his twenty police boys. The village constable, Omari, was a potent influence on his behalf, as was the headman, Assinditti, who could always count on Vandenburg to back his reasonable decisions in the conduct of the village. A good many of the elders, fat on the increased trade brought by the establishment of the post, and at ease in the peace insured by the presence of the armed police boys, could be depended on to use their influence whenever Vandenburg needed carriers, or canoe paddlers, or supplies for his expeditions. Vandenburg's magisterial decisions were avidly sought in matters arising from domestic tiffs, from cases of petty stealing, and weighty problems affecting property ownership. Vandenburg upheld with credit the dignity of Government in Susuba and throughout the whole district that centered on the Watumba River.

But on his side also the Reverend William Sanders had the backing of a considerable and influential party. His mission was situated a mile from Susuba village, and the material evidence of his success lay in his well-tended gardens, the church built of native materials by native workman, and the other buildings which served as house and schoolrooms.

His greatest strength, however, lay in the allegiance of Kekeape, an elderly native who had, in his middle age, been taken from Susuba to serve on an island-trading schooner. From the schooner, Kekeape, fired with a sense of adventure, had gone to work first on the plantations, later in the mines, and later still, for one of the young aviation companies that even then were beginning to develop New Guinea.

Somewhere along the line Kekeape had forsaken his belief in Buruma, the mountain at the back of the Watumba River inhabited by the spirits of the dead, and enthusiastically become a Christian. In his old age he returned to Susuba, to find his children grown and married, and rearing children.

The Reverend William was surprised and overjoyed to receive, from the outset of his mission, the wholehearted co-operation of Kekeape, not only in the work of converting the heathen but also as a tradesman. In an amazingly short space of time he had developed a strong following of believers who shifted their places of abode to the mission end of Susuba village and frowned on the social activities of the long house.

The first friction between Sanders and Vandenburg developed when the missionary, having formed a nucleus of support, advanced on the long house and seized, under the wondering eyes of the natives, a number of the carvings of heads and figures, and the carved council tables therein. He also took the skulls from the racks by the door, and, handing them out to his followers, marched with them up the village street toward the mission.

As soon as he had entered the long house, runners hurried to tell Vandenburg of the desecration; and thus, when Sanders led his procession through the village, the patrol officer intercepted him.

"Just where," he asked conversationally, "do you think you are going with those carvings?"

"My dear Mr. Vandenburg," said the Reverend Sanders, "I seem to detect some opposition in your voice. However, for your information, we are going to have a burning of idols. This will be a great day in the history of Susuba."

"It will be a great day, all right," Vandenburg said. "Because if you persist in what you are doing I'll have no other course than to put you under arrest for theft. Those are village treasures and they belong in the long house."

"Theft?" queried Sanders, raising his eyebrows.

"Theft," said Vandenburg. "I don't care what you do with your mission, but this is the village, and those are public property. Anyway, they aren't idols, as far as I've been able to make out. They're carvings. If you want them you buy them, and if there is even a single voice in the village says you can't have them, they stay in the long house."

" 'Thou shalt not make unto thee any graven image—' " began Sanders, but Vandenburg interrupted him.

"That's for you," he said. "Not for Susuba village, unless they hear the message for themselves."

Sanders' voice became oratorical, " 'Thus shall ye deal with them; ye shall destroy their altars, and break down their images, and cut down their groves, and burn their graven images with fire.' "

"I rather think not," the patrol officer said. "I'm administering the law here, and I see what you're doing as theft. Simple theft. And unless those things go back, I'm going to call Sergeant Tamari and six rifles and have him arrest you and your whole Christian community."

"But—" began the missionary.

"No 'buts,' " said Vandenburg. "While your men are putting those carvings back—and I hope they handle them with the respect they deserve—you might read Robert Louis Stevenson instead of Moses. Stevenson knew natives, and he didn't like the sort of thing you're doing now. 'Bloodier than a bombardment,' I think were his words. Don't destroy old habits. Just encourage new ones."

Vandenburg had other brushes with the missionary; notably on the occasion when he announced from the pulpit that it was illegal to fish on Sundays. When Vandenburg was apprised of the an-

nouncement by a deputation of distressed natives, he went into his
office and composed a letter. He wrote:

DEAR MR. SANDERS: You are possibly aware that the low-protein
diet of Susuba requires a constant inflow of fish in order that the
health level, particularly of the children, be maintained. You may
also be aware of the fact that in this climate it is impossible to keep
fish over Sunday. However, these things may not have occurred to
you when you recently announced the existence of a law which pre-
vents fishing on Sundays. I have made it clear to the people that no
such law exists, and that hereafter, as always, any announcement of
new laws will come through me.

Within limits, I am not concerned with the restrictions you may
place upon your converts. However, it would be as well if you made
it clear that any such restrictions are not initiated by the Government.

Sanders did not reply, nor did Vandenburg see him for a long
time after that. Yet in spite of this opposition of interests, each man
slowly developed a certain respect for the other when he was able
to judge him impersonally, from the results of his work. In Susuba
and elsewhere, Vandenburg maintained an honest administration,
and the people flourished under it.

Sanders' Christians were good clean people, and caused little
friction in the village, even though their houses clustered together
in a colony and they did not attend the village dances and other
celebrations.

Antagonism flared actively bright only when the missionary
sought to extend his influence into spheres of what Vandenburg
classified as temporal jurisdiction. But they were not very often at
loggerheads, perhaps because each of them left the village for long
periods upon their lawful pursuits, each extending and strengthen-

ing the influence of his work among the tribes of the river districts. To the Susuba mission on Sundays came a dribbling of two or sometimes three canoes from upriver; and Sanders dreamed sometimes of a day when the volume of this visitation would launch a considerable fleet.

To Susuba, during this period, came the explorer. He was a little man, aggressive, self-opinionated. He wore an enormous mustache which looked bigger because of his balding head, and he walked with a limp. He was armed with a battery of cameras and sporting rifles, and he traveled in a spick-and-span, ketch-rigged cruising yacht to which he never referred without using the personal pronoun "my." It was later revealed, however, that he had it on charter from the owner, a quiet Scot who cannily traveled with his property in the capacity of engineer.

The explorer limped up the little jetty and greeted Vandenburg, who had noted the arrival of the ketch and was waiting for him. He introduced himself by producing a card which identified him as "Captain E. Peddick," and with it he tendered a letter from His Excellency, the Administrator. His Excellency said that Captain Peddick intended to carry out a navigation of the Watumba River and its deeper tributaries, and that he would esteem it a favor to himself if his officers would extend the captain every reasonable facility.

Vandenburg, who had previously read of Peddick's exploits in the Antarctic, in South America and as manager of an anthropological expedition to northern Australia, was suitably impressed; but the rather bombastic small talk of the little man began to pall on him at lunchtime.

After he had extended all the usual courtesies, rather informally, Vandenburg paid a return visit to the ketch. She was beautifully found, crewed by ten or a dozen Solomon Islanders, boys of good physique who earned good money, if one could judge by the heavily ornamented leather belts with which they had equipped themselves, the hair peroxided and dyed in maroon and red and other fantastic shades, and the clean, good-quality clothing in which they were dressed.

In the hold were fifteen to twenty large cases of trade goods as well as an ample quantity of stores for the voyage. There were bales of red cloth and cases of bush knives, of mirrors and fishhooks, glass beads and razor blades—a well-chosen collection of articles such as the average native would trade his dearest possessions for.

"Are you thinking of buying up the river?" Vandenburg asked Peddick.

The little man stroked his big mustache. "There's quite an invest-ment there," he said. "Quite an investment. But after the Watumba we're going to tackle the Fly, and then the Sepik on the northern side. This is by way of getting our hands in, so to speak. No harm in trading, is there?"

"None at all," said Vandenburg. "I don't know, though, what you'll pick up. You wouldn't want to carry crocodile hides. There's nothing else here except for carvings. The people won't part with the best of them, and the best won't compare with the ordinary Middle Sepik or Trobriand work, which is the best in the Pacific, unless you have a fancy for Maori work, which is unprocurable anyway. It will be hard to get anything here to equal the value of your trade. Don't cheapen the value of the trade goods too much."

"I won't do that," said Peddick. "After the Fly and the Sepik trips, if we're still ahead of the monsoons, we may go over to the Trobriands and pick up pearl and trochus, perhaps, to cover some of our costs."

Vandenburg spent some time admiring the collection of heavy rifles which, with shotguns and light sporting rifles, Peddick had racked on the wall of the cabin. They were beautiful weapons, and he was frankly green with envy. But he couldn't feel that Peddick in the flesh lived up to the glamour of his considerable reputation.

He was, in fact, rather glad to see the last of the explorer when, on the following day, with half a dozen canoes in tow, Peddick's ketch vanished among the trees upriver. And for once he found himself in agreement with Sanders as they compared notes.

"I can't see what use an explorer would have for the Watumba," Sanders said. "An anthropologist, perhaps, but not an explorer. It's a nice, quiet, well-mapped river, with quiet people. It makes a fine excursion, but one would hardly call it exploring."

Nearly two weeks after the ketch had disappeared, a runner came to Vandenburg from the village of Birisip, high up the river, and the news he brought was disturbing.

"Sir," he said, in the lingua franca of the district, "the people of Birisip are unhappy that they have aroused the anger of the Government, and they want to know what it is they have done or what they have not done, and they will set it right."

Vandenburg said, "The Government is satisfied with the village of Birisip. There is no cause for complaint. What brings you?"

"Sir," said the villager, "a week ago the Government sent a white ship, and the people of the ship fired with rifles on the people of Birisip, and they, being very much afraid, ran into the bush. And when they returned, the council tables and the carving were gone from the long house, and certain pots, and some weapons that belonged to the men. Now the people of Birisip are unhappy about the council tables, and especially about a carving that sat in the inner chamber of the long house, for without this carving the initiation of the young men will lose some of its meaning, and the village some of its strength, and the young men will drift into loose ways."

"First," said Vandenburg, "you know that this is not the way of Government. The Government sent no ship up the river, and fired no rifles. Second, the man who did so was a thief, and shall be punished. And third, you shall have the carvings back for the long house when the thief is caught. In a little while I shall come to Birisip myself, and for what has been lost there will be a payment. I can say no more than this. But what of the shooting, the firing of rifles? Were any of the people hurt?"

"Truly, none," said the messenger.

"And was the fire returned?"

The messenger hung his head. "Sir, some of the young men went to the bend of the river, and as the ship went by, they fired at it with arrows, and it may be they hit a man. He was a native man, who worked in the crew of the boat, and he was struck in the shoulder. It was not a wound to do him much harm, sir."

"And at this bend in the river, did the arrows draw a return fire?" asked Vandenburg.

"Sir, there was a great deal of shooting," said the man. "But truly the shots were wild. They were not really aimed. It was just a firing at the trees, and it did no damage."

"Now, of this ship that went on up the river, have you heard further?" asked Vandenburg.

"At Mogidi, at Kobulumap, at Upi and beyond, the long houses were raided and the carvings stolen," said the messenger. "At Birisip and at Kobulumap, also, where the gardens are by the river, the gardens were raided, and the beans and plantains which were ready were taken for the ship. And at Birisip the crop of four betel-nut palms was taken for the men on the ship. The people of Birisip were troubled that the Government had taken their carvings, but at Kobulumap the people are angry, and they talk, talk, talk all the time about what they will do. And they have sent messengers to Mogidi and Birisip and Upi, and messengers have gone up the river. But the people of Birisip do not like the talk of the people of Kobulumap, and for this they have sent me to you."

"Now take this message," said Vandenburg, "to the people of Birisip, and take it there with all the speed you can. When the white boat comes again down the river, they are to go back into the bush and not appear, nor are they to shoot arrows from the trees any more. They are to send messages to Mogidi and Kobulumap and Upi and beyond, wherever the white boat has been, and tell them to go to the bush. And they must make it clear that the white boat is not the Government, and that the Government will take in hand the punishment of the men on the boat. If the white man goes ashore again at their villages, they are to make an accounting of their losses and tell them to me. And in a little while, when I come up the river next, I will come to them and I will do what I can. If the white boat has not returned by the day after tomorrow, I will come up the river. If the white boat comes here first, however, or if I meet it on the way, there will be other matters and I shall be delayed. No matter how long a time passes, I will come, and I will try to put this right. For it is a very great wrong, and the Government takes it much to heart."

With the messenger on his way, Vandenburg immediately set about the collection of stores for a protracted voyage upriver. But he had not been more than an hour on this task when Assinditti, the headman, came to tell him the ketch was in sight.

Vandenburg walked to the landing stage, and found the missionary already there, watching the ketch negotiate the river current. It swept downstream on the opposite side of the river and circled widely to come up to the stage. In a few brief sentences he told the missionary what he had learned from the messenger from Birisip. Sanders was shocked.

"On a peaceful river like the Watumba!" he said. "Heaven knows what the man might have started. No wonder Kobulumap is talking war. What are you going to do about it?"

"I don't know," said Vandenburg. "I think I'll get it well under control, though. He won't get away with it if I can help it."

"It's very worrying," said Sanders. "It's the kind of thing that all

sorry they didn't get Peddick. How's the serious one? You want medicines?"

"I've got everything on board that opens and shuts. No, I don't need help," said Gillies. "They're both recovering. The worst one got an arrow through the side, and he's on the mend. The other just had a slice through the shoulder. They'll do."

"I'd like to tie Peddick to the foremast and take him upriver again, slowly," Vandenburg said viciously. "He'll write a book about this and be a martyr, you wait and see."

When the unloading was finished, Vandenburg asked Gillies, "Who does the trade belong to, you or Peddick?"

"Peddick," said Gillies.

"Right," said Vandenburg. "Now, there's a small matter of compensation for possibly wounded villagers, for crops stolen and for native artifacts lost on the voyage."

"You'll find everything on the wharf except for a few arrows shot off at birds and things," Gillies said.

"Not when I ask at the villages, I won't. I'll find they are short of more than I have to give back. I've got to make compensation for the threat to their peace, for time lost from hunting and the gardens, for a lot of wounded dignity. So, I'll have the trade goods, too. Get them up on the wharf, and I'll see they go to the right place."

"Don't blame you," said Gillies. "I can see I don't have to make any suggestions—but what about the rifles? Any chance that you can confiscate them?"

"I ought to," said Vandenburg. "I'll take them in custody. And, by the way, I'll have to come back with you to Moresby. A written report won't cover this."

While the Solomon Islanders were unloading the trade goods, Vandenburg went to find the missionary, from whom, for the first time, he needed a favor. On the way he called in at a hut at the

Christian end of the village where Kekeape lay dying, for he admired and respected the old man. Melanesians are not afraid of death and, as he half expected, he found Kekeape looking forward to the new experiences to which he felt death would bring him.

They talked quietly, in friendliness, for a little while, but Kekeape did not have much strength and Vandenburg soon left him.

After he had told the missionary of the steps he had taken, he sat down and outlined his requirement.

"I'll have to go to Moresby with the ketch," he said. "There'll be an inquiry, and probably a court case, although from the point of view of the Administration it may be as well to avoid the publicity this is going to bring. Still, one way or another, they'll need me and my evidence and I can't send Peddick in under a native escort. But with the river people using arrows—properly aroused, I take it—I can't afford to let things drift at this end. I think from your point of view this could help you, too. I'll detail a corporal and six men for you, and leave the sergeant in charge at Susuba. The corporal will go with you and you can use my stores, and I'll see that your expenses are covered. You can take the carvings back to the villages, restore their belongings and pay compensation from Peddick's trade. Not too much compensation, by the way. Just what you think is fair. And I want you to take depositions from witnesses. If you see it my way, it could strengthen your influence upriver. And I'd always be prepared to return the favor wherever I could. What do you say about it?"

"I'll only be too happy," Sanders said. "That is, I agree with some of it. I'll go up the river and restore the peace and I'll take back some of the goods and compensate with the trade, and write out the depositions. But I won't take the idols."

"Oh, Bill," said Vandenburg frowning—they seldom used names at all, but they had got to the acceptance of first names a long time before—"you can't take that attitude, surely. These are their possessions, they need them, and they wouldn't part with them. Anyway, I doubt that they are idols. They are symbols that help to hold the villages together. They must go back with the rest or we betray our trust."

"There is a providence in this," said the missionary stubbornly. "Through the hands of this Captain Peddick all the villages of the river have lost their idols. They should not be returned but replaced by the true worship of God. I could not see my way clear to take them back."

Vandenburg tilted his chair back, looking at the missionary. Suddenly he sat up and said, "Come with me and see old Kekeape."

The missionary looked at him. "That's an abrupt change, Carl."

"Not really. I want to show you something. I called in on him on my way here. There's something going on I'd like you to see."

They walked together to the house of Kekeape.

"Don't make any comment," said Vandenburg. "The old man's near the end of his journey."

Inside the house, Kekeape lay quietly on the hard wooden planks of his bed. His head was raised, and his weak eyes, as yet unglazed, were watching the movements of his granddaughter, a pretty young woman, who worked about him. She was fastening circlets of native workmanship about his calves, setting anklets into place. Old Kekeape, lined and weary of life, was wearing the badges and adornments of his heathen youth. Every now and then, he spoke sharply to the girl, croaking out instructions to make this or that adjustment to his dress.

The two men watched for only a moment, then Vandenburg took Sanders by the arm and they walked out of the hut.

"I don't understand," said Sanders. "What was it you wanted me to see?"

Vandenburg called to one of a group of men standing silently near by.

"Kevi," he said, "your grandfather, old Kekeape, is dying."

"Yes, sir," said Kevi. "He will be dead tonight."

"Kevi, will you tell me why your grandfather is having himself dressed in the manner of his youth?"

The young man smiled uncertainly, then looked away quickly and traced patterns with his bare toe in the dust.

"Kevi, tell me why he dresses as though he wants to go to Buruma instead of Heaven? Is he not dressed for Buruma, Kevi?"

Kevi did not answer, but the missionary gave a startled gasp. Kevi was looking at the mountains where the high peak of Buruma, the mountain reserved for the spirits of the dead, overshadowed its neighbors.

Vandenburg continued his questioning, "Is Kekeape a Christian, Kevi, or is he a heathen?"

Kevi looked up smartly at that, surprised at the question.

"Oh, sir, he's a true Christian. He is truly a Christian, more a Christian than any other man of the village."

"There is no such thing as being more or less of a Christian," said the missionary. He spoke pedantically, but his face had become worried.

"If Kekeape's a true Christian, tell me why he dresses to go to Buruma," persisted Vandenburg.

"He is true. He is going to Heaven. No matter how you dress, you can go to Heaven," said Kevi.

"True," said Vandenburg. "But he dresses to go to Buruma."

"Sir, it is this way," Kevi said: "He is an old man, and many things are uncertain. He is a Christian and will go to Heaven. Yet he is not certain of that road above the clouds to Heaven. It is a road he cannot see. And if he misses his way, then he will go to Buruma, the mountain of the spirits, which we can see there behind us. He has known Buruma and the road that leads to Buruma all his life, sir. But truly he will try to find the road to Heaven first."

"Good heavens!" said the Reverend Sanders. He plunged his face into his hands, then turned his back and started to walk hastily to the hut where Kekeape lay, but stopped again and turned around.

"Master Sanders," Kevi said, "Kekeape is in good hands. He has told us these things. Do not misunderstand him. He is properly dressed for Buruma, but he goes to Heaven."

The missionary left the others, and began to walk back to the mission. Vandenburg hurried a few steps and caught up with him.

"Do you think that Kekeape is not a Christian?" he asked.

"I don't know. I don't know what to think," Sanders said, and his face was working convulsively. "My best helper. The man I was so sure of."

"You can still be sure," said Vandenburg. "I think Kevi is right. Kekeape is a Christian. I think perhaps you can find some comfort in history. The Christians, the first of them, carried over a lot of pagan practices after they found Christ. Christmas, for example, and Easter. All sorts of things. You can't expect Kekeape to be stronger than those people."

"Carl, old friend," said Sanders—and Vandenburg was aware that the appellation carried deep meaning—"I must go away a little while. I must think. I have been wrong, and I don't know where."

"I'll leave it in your hands," said Vandenburg. "I have to go soon, and I will leave it up to you. It is, after all, a matter of your conscience. But the people need their carvings, in some way. Don't worry about Kekeape. He is a good man."

"That it should be Kekeape," said the missionary slowly. "Perhaps I should see this, too, as the workings of providence. It is very difficult, my friend. I am not worrying about Kekeape. I am worrying about myself, for Kekeape is a good man, but it was to me he looked, and from me he learned." He stopped talking and faced Vandenburg. "Will you leave me, Carl? I must think."

Vandenburg held out his hand and Sanders took it. "I'll see you in a month," said the patrol officer.

"I will be looking forward to it," said the missionary, and he meant it.

And when Vandenburg came back to the Watumba River he found the idols each in its own long house in the villages by the river. And in Birisip and Mogidi and Kobulumap he found happiness in the hearts of the people, and from the nearer villages long lines of canoes came down each week to the services at Susuba Mission.

The Village Road

A MAN *with a turtle carried on his shoulder came hasting along the sun-dappled track. He was hurrying into the evening; hurrying from the sea to his village; hurrying from his work to his reward; his hips circling, his feet twinkling in the racing style of the competitive walker; and hurrying with him was the evanescent flavor of romance, so that the compulsion took me to look behind and watch his happy hurrying figure; and I thought, and for the first time, that in this moment was crystallized the very spirit of romance, this moment of transition; the moment when the fish rests before the leap, when the dragon-fly hovers, and the butterfly's wings are stilled; the moment when the colt quivers under the first touch of the rope, when the new ship is poised upon the slipway, when the child first enters the school gate, when the maid abandons her lips to the first kiss of a lover. It is the moment of transition, the moment of impact, the moment of truth.*

The grass-grown track meandered between village and village, running along the seacoast, and from time to time joined with other tracks which opened up the villages of the hinterland. It was the artery of life upon the island, and in this evening hour it served a multitude: long files of women returning from the waterholes, each bearing on her head a basket piled high with a dozen or more brown-black bottles made cunningly from coconuts; women from

269

the gardens, bearing taro and yams; women from the forest, with great bundles of dry wood chosen to burn without fury and without smoke inside the houses.

The children came in scattered droves, some clinging to their mothers, some alone, some in shouting competitive gangs. Some carried bush knives as big as themselves; industrious little girls carried the family wood supply, an embryo pater familias brought a string of his own little fish, a ten-year-old nursemaid built a raucous squeaker from a coconut leaf to pacify a spoiled baby brother. One girl walked with a tethered birdwing butterfly, the huge emerald-green and black Troides prianus, its fat golden body firmly tied with a halter of pandanus thread that, at the other end of its two-foot length was looped to the captor's wrist, so that the living jewel fluttered about her head and shoulders, desperate in its efforts at escape.

In her other hand the girl carried her butterfly net, a loop of green vine in the shape of a tennis racquet, the open head filled with a once-dainty net of spider web, now gapped and torn from the insect's furious struggles. She was a beautiful little girl, with breasts that were unformed buds, her brown hair not frizzled, but lightly waved, her skirt, a hand's breadth length of banana fiber, dyed red and yellow and deep off-black. Her eyes were brilliant with the elation of childhood, and in her the cruelty and the beauty of childhood gleamed like the bright sheen of the butterfly.

The men, too, came and went, some walking inland with fish, some heading for the coastal villages with yams, or pandanus fiber for nets, or leaves for sails, or wood fit for carving. Most of them stopped when they saw me, and tendered the island greeting.

"Avaka, Taubada. Where you going?"

"I'm going to Losuia."

"What you going to Losuia for, Taub'?"

"I'm going to post a letter."

"All right, Taubada. Okay."

Nor was this curiosity only. It was a polite greeting, implying that my business was of importance to the rest of the island, as was the business of everyone who lived there. It made the inquirer a bringer of news: "The Dim-dim Taubada went today to Losuia, to post a letter." It brought me into the community; and where the greeting was applied to those who were of the community by right of birth, it helped to knit the member components into a cohesive whole. As a greeting it had meaning; far more meaning than the European salutations, "Good day," "How do you do?" Good day indeed—everyone can tell it is a good day. And the islander is not much concerned with health, for he enjoys it as a matter of right. Much better to feel that someone is interested in your movements, finds them of importance, discusses them, correlates them with the movements of others. And from your answer forms an estimate of your character.

The Government man rejects the greeting with a stony indignation. "Cheeky niggers, these," he says. "I'll teach them a lesson." And at the first excuse he jails a dozen or two, to help him maintain the roads.

The arrest, too, indicates a moment of impact, a moment of transition. And the whole island is reeling under another, older impact of which the shock waves have not yet receded: the impact of civilized man upon his underdeveloped brother.

For the track, from the village to the garden, from the sea to the hinterland, is part of a larger road we all have traveled through time, the road up through the centuries, leading—how can we tell where it leads? To start, we must know where we are; and then, if only we know where we have come from, we may have a fair idea in what direction, at least, we are going. And in the absence of a perfectly comprehended destination, this is the only way.

For us at the moment there is only the road, and if we must know in what direction we have lately traveled, then we must also find out just where we once stood upon it. Well, here are these people, and presumably they are a long way back upon the track. They have not yet invented the wheel; and in fact they have not yet comprehended a use for it. They have no metal, except for the poor samples of steel which the trader exchanges for the wealth of their copra and the beauty of the shell they fish up from the cool ocean depths. But here, on this island, they have learned to live in peace and amity; their neighbors are understood, their children are loved, their aged enjoy a friendly respect, their sick are nursed, and not in special institutions where for money the responsibility of all is shouldered by a few. Look, if you can, upon this man who comes from the trade store, carrying tobacco he has paid for with coconuts from his palms.

A cancer has eaten away his face from the bridge of his nose to his chin, and the ravages extend over his cheeks. The last remnants of his teeth are obviously useless to him. You can see, if you can bear to look, the tongue bobbling about at the back of that horrid cavern which is his mouth. Yet he is well nourished, and his companions do not shudder at the thought of his company. Someone has chewed his food for him these many months past. He lives his full life, not in an institution, not maintained conveniently out of sight, but in the heart of his community; and he is not denied the daily love and affection and comradeship which is the due of every man. Nor does he feel himself an encumbrance, for he performs the normal work that is within his power. Is this something we left long behind on the road to civilization? I think it is.

He and his fellows worship a kindly god, a god in human image who walks among men. He is a god without forgiveness; but a god who makes few demands so that in Tuma, the Heaven of the island, the evil man, the seeker for power, the plotter flourish, as they did among their companions when they walked the earth. Life goes on without much change in the island Heaven, a testimonial to the islander's appreciation of the goodness of God upon earth.

And the chiefs of the island rule without the necessity for fear. Their symbol of power is not the scepter or the mace; but the yam, the staple foodstuff of the island. Their wives are not wives, but representatives of the people, chosen one from each village as we choose politicians. Their sons do not inherit, so that with every change of rulers there is a change of dynasty, and yet the dynasty remains unchanged, in the same association of blood. It is the son of the chief's sister—the son of a commoner—who inherits.

And so one could go on, piling detail upon detail; and in discovering where these people stand upon the road that leads to the future of humanity one could, possibly, lose faith in the tenet that we have advanced. Were we, before we discovered the wheel, as advanced as this?—as skilled in the arts of poetry and song, and the dance, and carving; as competent in navigation, as familiar with the stars and the seasons, as self-sufficient, as considerate? If we were, and it is possible, then we have developed our transport facilities at the expense of our basic philosophy. We have lost something, gained something; and there are times when we and the islanders differ hardly at all.

Watch the girl who follows behind the man with the cancerous mouth. She holds all beauty within her body, poised and slender. Her skin is agleam with the fresh oil of coconuts, and spangled with the glittering gold of the coconut pollen for which she lately had her lover climb one of the tall palms that border the track. A bracelet of white cowries proclaims her an aristocrat, and tucked within it is a sprig of vana, highly scented, and denoting that she looks for love. She has painted her face with a tiny, effective design of jetty black and glittering white, a small froth of simple curves encircling one eye and arching over her forehead; and seeing this, everyone must know that for a brief holiday season she has fore-

sworn work and seeks amusement. There are fresh-plucked flowers in a pattern on her hair.

Her skirt, of soft grays and greens and yellows, is much too short for the skirt of a good girl, and sits low on her hips, balanced so precariously there that it seems the dainty stateliness of her walk is designed solely to keep it in position; that is, if you do not know that when her holiday is over she will return to carrying heavy weights on the crown of her head.

She has spent hours upon her toilette, assisted probably by some less lucky but unenvious friend. And she is the girl who walks down Bond Street or Fifth Avenue; mistress of her destiny, well brought up and now left to her own devices. The many thousand years between her and her sisters have brought only material changes—she values above diamonds the sapi-sapi shell jewelry that gleams rose-red at her ears and throat, and the white shell garters she wears below her knees.

There is a king upon the island, and a king's messenger, and a keeper of the archives, and chiefs and councilors; yet it is an island without a police force, without an army; an island remarkably free from troubles of state. An island with a history and a constitution; but without professors and schools.

So, standing on this track, on this island, watching these people at their quiet occasions, one could be deluded into believing that we have not come far upon the road that leads from antiquity through civilization to an unknown destiny. But this island is one of a group, and beyond the group are other islands, and beyond them are more again, until we come to the greatest island of them all, New Guinea, a fantastic conglomeration of people so diversified that a story which is true of one corner of the island may be laughed to scorn in an adjoining valley; an island where five hundred separate languages and their dialects are spoken by people who have never learned to communicate with their unrelated neigh-

bors. And nearly all these people are now, in this year, in this century, at the moment of impact, the moment of truth, the moment of transition. Or they soon will be; or they lately were. Not all of them are gentle, not all have discovered the arts, not all have grace or beauty.

You can test this moment of transition at a tiny village on the main range north of Kairuku, where the locals wear no clothes at all. In recent years, church workers at a mission on that coast made little robes of unbleached calico and when the simple naked ladies arrived at church, each was handed a garment to be worn during the service, and handed back at its close. The missionaries took no such precautions with the men, who must have gained thereby a somewhat confused impression of the import of the looming civilization.

You can see it in sophisticated Port Moresby, where Government wrestles with the problems of position and protocol. Not long ago a resident accosted a garbageman, a wild tribesman recently recruited from the Central Highlands of the country. He carried a garbageman's ordinary sack on his back, but this sack was agitated with convulsive movements.

"What have you got in there?" the resident asked.

"Food, Taubada. Only food."

The resident investigated. When he opened the sack a little child ran for safety.

But if that incident had some less horrifying import, as probably it had, why I have seen at Wagamush, on the upper reaches of the mighty and mysterious Sepik River, still other evidence that this is the moment of impact, in the bullet wounds scarring the skins of savage tribesmen.

I have seen the heads of men, freshly collected for the necessities of ceremonial. I have walked in a village where, lately, a little boy could have been bought for the equivalent, in shells, of five dollars.

A chief had bought such a one, of an age with his own son, and the two naked babies played happily together, with one differentiation only—that the chief's son was armed with a bone dagger. Soon or late, with the approval of his family, he would kill his playmate and, having taken his head, would be admitted thus early into the councils of the tribe.

In the distance we have traveled from the spot where these people stand, the social sanctions have greatly changed; but the people are the same. You will find in the most primitive villages the miser and the spendthrift, the fighter and the man of peace, the tradesman happy in the work of his hands, the artist, the philosopher, the entertainer, the careful housewife, the harlot, the philanderer, and the fool, all living together in the one community as in our own; some cruel, some kind, some honest, some unreliable, passionate, phlegmatic, iconoclastic, sincere—the same mixture, in a similar incalculable proportion that you are likely to find in any non-specialized community anywhere in the wide world.

They are, in short, people; though among the incoming Europeans who have made the initial impact there is a disturbing tendency to regard them as intelligent animals of a lesser genus, or as subjects for the delectation of anthropologists, or as museum pieces. They are thoughtfully enjoined to become as the newcomers themselves as soon as possible, and at the same time inhibited from doing so by a variety of economic and educational devices.

The students who earnestly put these indigenes and their reactions in a jellied agglomeration upon the slide of their questing microscopes have been variously concerned in establishing their racial origins; and the resultant theories, based on a turn of language here, a blood group there, a political, social or religious inheritance in many an unsuspected corner, place these origins almost anywhere in the known world.

The peculiarities of individual tribes have grown from their en-

vironment, and particularly from the isolation of a few similarly minded types; and nowhere in the world is there a country so suited to the segregation of peoples. Particularly this is because, as d'Albertis once wrote, "It is easier to climb the highest Alp than to cross an ordinary hill in New Guinea." But partly also it is because this was a country without economic fears, in which any man of ability, willing to devote himself to his tasks, could take his family's living from the land or the abundantly bountiful seas. He had little need of commerce.

Without the economic fear Government, which can exist only with the help of some fear, was compelled to introduce physical fears and, through a variety of religions, some good, some bad, metaphysical fears by which the communities could be welded into units of interdependent members.

The European, in his Twentieth Century assistance to the country, has removed the physical and metaphysical guards on communal behavior, and today, with occasional success, he is endeavoring to bring economic fear to their replacement. In the betwixt and between the vagaries of human nature released have a fruitful development. This, too, in a number of anti-social manifestations, is a by-product of the moment of impact, and incidentally affords unlimited opportunities to the man who likes to observe his fellow mortals.

But perhaps the greatest attraction New Guinea holds for such a man lies in its effect upon other Europeans like himself, who, in these primeval forests and on these timeless shores are isolated in communities of which a typical one would consist of perhaps a dozen Twentieth Century people living out their lives against the brown, amorphous background of a thousand natives who, among them, carry out all the work necessary for existence and relieve their masters of all but the most cogent responsibilities and anxieties.

This is the writer's paradise, this country under violent change. It reels today under the crushing contempt of the new for the old, under a load of intolerance and misunderstanding. Among the indigenes the parents fight against the children turning irresistibly to the new day. Among the importation the teachers who could learn a little from their pupils are dulled by prejudice.

That is the way I see New Guinea, a country at the moment of impact, the moment of transition, hurrying, hurrying like the man with the turtle on his shoulder; the turtle feebly swimming its flippers through the unresistant air, and the man hurrying, with only a backward glance for the road he has traveled. He is muscled like an athlete, and beautiful in the scented evening; and he is single-minded in his mission. Tomorrow the turtle will be eaten, and in a month its shell will adorn the pierced ears of women; and there will be another mission, another day, and another scented night.

Date Due

Date Due			
JAN 6 1958			
FEB 28 1958			
MAR 22 1958			
	PRINTED IN U. S. A.		